ECLECTIC ENGLISH CLASSICS

Addison's Sir Roger de Coverley (Underwood)

Arnold's Sohrab and Rustum (Tanner)

Bunyan's Pilgrim's Progress (Jones and Arnold)

Burke's Conciliation with America (Clark)
Speeches at Bristol (Bergin)

Burns's Poems—Selections (Venable)

Byron's Childe Harold (Canto IV), Prisoner of Chillon, Mazeppa, and other Selections (Venable)

Carlyle's Essay on Burns (Miller)

Chaucer's Prologue and Knighte's Tale (Van Dyke)

Coleridge's Ancient Mariner (Garrigues)

Cooper's Pilot (Watrous)
The Spy (Barnes)

Defoe's History of the Plague in London (Syle)
Robinson Crusoe (Stephens)

De Quincey's Revolt of the Tartars

Dickens's Christmas Carol and Cricket on the Hearth (Wannamaker)
Tale of Two Cities (Pearce)

Dryden's Palamon and Arcite (Bates)

Eliot's Silas Marner (McKitrick)

Emerson's American Scholar, Self-Reliance, Compensation (Smith)

Franklin's Autobiography (Reid)

Goldsmith's Vicar of Wakefield (Hansen)

Gray's Elegy in a Country Churchyard, and Goldsmith's Deserted Village (Van Dyke)

Hughes's Tom Brown's School Days (Gosling).

Irving's Sketch Book—Selections (St. John)
Tales of a Traveler (Rutland)

Lincoln's Addresses and Letters (Moores)
Address at Cooper Union; and Macaulay's Speeches on Copyright (Pittenger)

Macaulay's Essay on Addison (Matthews)
Essay on Milton (Mead)
Essays on Lord Clive and Warren Hastings (Holmes)

(S.95b)

Macaulay's Lays of Ancient Rome and other Poems (Atkinson)
Life of Johnson (Lucas)
Speeches on Copyright; and Lincoln's Address at Cooper Union (Pittenger)

Milton's L'Allegro, Il Penseroso, Comus, Lycidas (Buck)
Paradise Lost. Books I and II (Stephens)

Old Ballads (Morton)

Old Testament Narratives (Baldwin)

Poe's Selected Poems and Tales (Stott)

Pope's Homer's Iliad. Books I, VI, XXII, XXIV
Rape of the Lock, and Essay on Man (Van Dyke)

Ruskin's Sesame and Lilies (Rounds)

Scott's Abbot
Ivanhoe (Schreiber)
Lady of the Lake (Bacon)
Marmion (Coblentz)
Quentin Durward (Norris)
Woodstock

Shakespeare's As You Like It (North)
Hamlet (Shower)
Henry V (Law)
Julius Caesar (Baker)
Macbeth (Livengood)
Merchant of Venice (Blakely)
Midsummer Night's Dream (Haney)
The Tempest (Barley)
Twelfth Night (Weld)

Southey's Life of Nelson

Stevenson's Inland Voyage, and Travels with a Donkey (Armstrong)
Treasure Island (Fairley)

Swift's Gulliver's Travels (Gaston)

Tennyson's Idylls of the King. Selections (Willard)
Princess (Shryock)

Thackeray's Henry Esmond (Bissell)

Washington's Farewell Address, and Webster's First Bunker Hill Oration (Lewis)

Webster's Bunker Hill Orations

Wordsworth's Poems—Selections (Venable)

Washington Irving.

ECLECTIC ENGLISH CLASSICS

SELECTIONS

FROM

IRVING'S SKETCH-BOOK

EDITED BY

ROBERT P. ST. JOHN

THE COMMERCIAL HIGH SCHOOL
BROOKLYN, N. Y.

NEW YORK ·:· CINCINNATI ·:· CHICAGO
AMERICAN BOOK COMPANY

INTRODUCTION.

WASHINGTON IRVING, the eighth and youngest son of William and Sarah Irving, was born in a house on William Street, in New York City, April 3, 1783. His father was a descendant of an old Orkney family, and his mother was a native of Falmouth, England. Young Washington began his school days at the age of four. At the age of sixteen his school days were over, and he began the study of law. Though his education was of a rudimentary and incomplete character, consisting of a smattering of Latin, music, and the ordinary English branches, he gave early signs of a natural avidity for reading, and of a power of rapidly assimilating what he read. Sinbad, Robinson Crusoe, and Gulliver made a deep impression on his young mind. His early fondness for romance showed itself in many ways, and the theater in John Street possessed for him a seductive charm, to which he succumbed as often as he could steal away from home; for his father, of the stern ways and habits of the Scotch Covenanter, looked upon theaters with hearty disfavor. In 1802 he entered the law office of Josiah Ogden Hoffman, and, together with his " Blackstone," he read general literature voraciously. About this time his health began to fail, and he made frequent trips up the Hudson and the Mohawk, to Ogdensburg, Montreal, Albany, Schenectady, and Saratoga. While in Judge Hoffman's office, he offset the tedium of his studies by writing, over the name of " Jonathan Oldstyle," a series of papers for the " Morning Chronicle," a newspaper planned on the style of the " Spectator " and " Tatler." His health continuing poor, in May he went to Europe, spent six weeks in Bordeaux, studying the language, seeing life, and enlarging the scope of his powers of observation. Then he visited the Mediterranean, gathering more material, seeing new cities, studying the strong characters he met. Sicily, Genoa, Naples, Rome, came beneath his eye, and he saw Nelson's fleet spreading its sails for Trafalgar. At Rome a critical epoch in his life occurred. The atmosphere of music, of which he was passionately fond, of art, and especially painting, all tended to work powerfully on the artistic side of his nature, and appealed strongly to the poetic temperament, that, in spite of his keen sense of humor, was deep within him. At this time, and in this atmosphere, he met Washington Allston, the artist, and was almost persuaded by him to take up art; but Irving, convinced that his inclination was more the effect of his present surroundings than of a deep latent artistic power within himself, refrained, and continued his journey, seeking new faces and new scenes. Irving was essentially a traveler. He saw at a glance all those peculiarities and oddities of form and character that attract and amuse; and he had a happy way of putting up with inconveniences, getting the best out of everything that came before his notice, and entering thoroughly into the spirit of his surroundings. Switzerland, the Netherlands, Paris, London, were in turn visited. In London he saw John Kemble, Cooke, and Mrs. Siddons. In February, 1806, he returned to this country, and was admitted to the bar, but he never practiced law. He soon engaged, with his brother William and James K. Paulding, in the issue (1807) of a humorously satirical semi-monthly periodical called " Salmagundi, or the Whim-Whams and Opinions of Launcelot Langstaff, Esq., and Others." It was quite successful in its local hits, and in it Irving first awoke to a conception of his power. In 1809 appeared the droll " History of New York by Diedrich Knickerbocker. From the Beginning of the World to the End of the Dutch Dynasty." It won for its author instant fame. The book was cleverly advertised before it appeared, the newspapers containing descriptions of a gentleman named Diedrich Knickerbocker, who was said to have mysteriously disappeared without paying his board bill, but leaving behind him a curious manuscript which his creditor was about to publish. Just before the book was completed, Irving underwent the great anguish of his life. The second daughter of Judge Hoffman, Matilda, with whom he was in love, died in her eighteenth year. He remained true to her memory, and never married. The " Knickerbocker History " was highly praised by Scott, who recognized its merit, and detected in it strong resemblances to the style of Swift. The work was begun by Washington and his brother Peter as a travesty on Dr. Samuel Mitchell's " Handbook of New York;" but Peter sailed for Europe when five chapters only were completed, and left Washington to finish the work. The next year (1810) Washington became a silent partner, with a fifth interest, in the commercial house established in New York and Liverpool by his brothers, and (1813–14) was editorially connected with the " Analectic Magazine " of Philadelphia, and contributed a number of biographical sketches of American naval commanders. In 1814 he served four months as aide-de-camp and military secretary to Gov. Tompkins, and in 1815 sailed again for Europe. About this time financial troubles began to gather over the business house; and Washington, on arriving in England, found his brother Peter ill, and thus considerable work of a commercial nature devolved upon him. Yet in the midst of business cares he found time for quiet rovings through Warwickshire and other parts of England, gathering material for "The Sketch-Book," and mingling in society with the literary men of the time. But the business troubles of the house increased, and 1816 and 1817 were anxious years. It was in the latter year that he met Scott in his home at Abbotsford, and felt the charm of his family circle. In 1818 the house went into bankruptcy. Irving, declining a clerkship in the Navy Department, and deferring an editorship which Scott held out to him, preferred to follow his own literary pursuits, and brought out "The Sketch-Book" (1819) in America. It was unqualifiedly successful; and Irving, who had heretofore been held as the ornamental feature of the family, became its financial stay, graciously returning the kind favors of earlier days. Irving offered "The Sketch-Book" to Murray & Constable for republication; but they declined it, in spite of Scott's recommendation. Irving then started to publish it himself, but, his publisher failing, its issue was stopped. Scott induced Murray to buy it for two hundred pounds, which was doubled on the success of the book. In 1820 Irving was in Paris, and in 1821 wrote "Bracebridge Hall," bringing it out in 1822. This year he was in Dresden. He returned to Paris in 1823, and the next year brought out "Tales of a Traveller." It was severely criticised. The year 1826 found him in Madrid as *attaché* of the legation commissioned by A. H. Everett, United States minister to Spain, to translate various documents relating to Columbus, collected by Navarrete; and from this work Irving produced (1828) the "History of the Life and Voyages of Christopher Columbus." For it he got three thousand guineas, and the fifty-guinea medal offered by George IV. for historical composition. A pleasant sojourn in the south of Spain gave him further insight into Spanish lore, and in 1829 the " Chronicles of the Conquest of Granada " was given to the public. In the quiet seclusion of the Alhambra, the same year, he wove a portion of that graceful fabric which he gave the world in 1832. While in the Alhambra he received word of his appointment as secretary to the legation at London, and, reluctantly accepting it, returned there. In 1831 appeared his " Companions of Columbus," and the same year he received from Oxford the degree of LL.D. The next year he returned to New York, after a foreign sojourn of seventeen years, and was welcomed with tremendous enthusiasm. He bought Sunnyside, below Tarrytown on the Hudson, and prepared to settle quietly down to literary work ; but the restless spirit of travel he had imbibed abroad induced him to take a flying trip through the West before doing so, and the summer of the same year found him with Commissioner Ellsworth, interested in the removal of the Indian tribes across the Mississippi. The literary outcome of this digression was the " Tour on the Prairies," which came out in 1835. With it came also " Abbotsford " and " Newstead Abbey," and the " Legends of the Conquest of Spain," making up the " Crayon Miscellany." In 1836 came " Astoria ;" and from 1839 to 1841 he contributed articles for the " Knickerbocker Magazine," which were afterward gathered into " Wolfert's Roost " (1855). From 1842 to 1846 Irving was United States minister to Spain. Returning to his home, he spent the remaining years of his life at Sunnyside, engaged in literary work, chiefly the " Life of Mahomet " and the " Life of Washington." The final volume of this last was completed only three months before he died. He passed away at Sunnyside, Nov. 28, 1859.

Washington Irving was the first American who was admitted by Englishmen on equal terms into the great republic of letters. By him American literature was enriched in form and elegance, and its scope enlarged. He opened the treasure-house of Spanish history and romance, and gave an impulse to historical and biographical research. As an historian and biographer, his conclusions were carefully drawn, and just, and have stood the test of time.

Possessed of a broad and genial nature, a rich poetic temperament, a fancy that was as nimble as it was sprightly, a facile and ornate power of vivid and graphic description, and a pure and graceful style that rivals that of Addison, he was the very prince of story-tellers and the most fascinating of fireside companions. His delicacy of touch was equal to the task of adding beauty to the exquisite tracery of the Alhambra, and his refined imagination revivified the romantic legends of Granada, while his genial humor created a cherished ancestry for his native city. With such inimitable drollery did he place in succession upon his canvas the Dutch forefathers of New Amsterdam, that Diedrich Knickerbocker, fleeing through the dormer-windowed streets of New York, left behind him the legacy of a name as real and as enduring as that of Peter Stuyvesant.

Yet it is in "The Sketch-Book," perhaps, more than in any other of his works, that the qualities of style and mind which have so characterized Washington Irving, and endeared him to English-reading people, appear in their freshest, most varied form, covering a wider range of humanity, bubbling over with a humor that seems to have the inexhaustible spontaneity of a spring. Here drollery, grace, pathos, grandeur, in turn touch the heart and move the fancy. A broad, genial atmosphere pervades it, fresh and open as the blue sky, in which its characters live, move, and have their being, drawn with a portraiture as real as life, and with a gentle satire that has no trace of bitterness.

It is "The Sketch-Book" that affords such charming glimpses of the good old English Christmas, and such graceful reflections, under the shadow of the venerable Abbey; while with its tatterdemalion Rip Van Winkle, and its soft but timid-hearted pedagogue Ichabod Crane, it is "The Sketch-Book" which has given to our noble Hudson the weird witchery of legend, charming as the blue outline of the Catskills, and fascinating as the shades of Sleepy Hollow.

CONTENTS.

THE SKETCH-BOOK.

THE AUTHOR'S ACCOUNT OF HIMSELF.

" I am of this mind with Homer, that as the snaile that crept out of her shel was turned eftsoones [1] into a toad, and thereby was forced to make a stoole to sit on ; so the traveller that stragleth from his owne country is in a short time transformed into so monstrous a shape, that he is faine to alter his mansion with his manners, and to live where he can, not where he would."

LYLY's Euphues.[2]

I WAS always fond of visiting new scenes, and observing strange characters and manners. Even when a mere child I began my travels, and made many tours of discovery into foreign parts and unknown regions of my native city, to the frequent alarm of my parents, and the emolument of the town-crier. As I grew into boyhood, I extended the range of my observations. My holiday afternoons were spent in rambles about the surrounding country. I made myself familiar with all its places famous in history or fable. I knew every spot where a murder or robbery had been committed, or a ghost seen. I visited the neighboring villages, and added greatly to my stock of knowledge by noting their habits and customs, and conversing with their sages and great men. I even journeyed one long summer's day to the

---

[1] Speedily; at once.

[2] John Lyly, Lylie, Lyllie, or Lilly (1553–1609) was an English wit and writer of Shakespeare's time. He wrote several plays, but is best known from his novel Euphues, the style of which was intended to reform and purify that of the English language. This book immediately became the rage in the court circles, and for many years was the court standard.

summit of the most distant hill, from whence I stretched my eye over many a mile of *terra incognita*, and was astonished to find how vast a globe I inhabited.

This rambling propensity strengthened with my years. Books of voyages and travels became my passion; and, in devouring their contents, I neglected the regular exercises of the school. How wistfully would I wander about the pier-heads in fine weather, and watch the parting ships, bound to distant climes! With what longing eyes would I gaze after their lessening sails, and waft myself in imagination to the ends of the earth!

Further reading and thinking, though they brought this vague inclination into more reasonable bounds, only served to make it more decided. I visited various parts of my own country; and, had I been merely influenced by a love of fine scenery, I should have felt little desire to seek elsewhere its gratification, for on no country have the charms of Nature been more prodigally lavished. Her mighty lakes, like oceans of liquid silver; her mountains, with their bright aerial tints; her valleys, teeming with wild fertility; her tremendous cataracts, thundering in their solitudes; her boundless plains, waving with spontaneous verdure; her broad, deep rivers, rolling in solemn silence to the ocean; her trackless forests, where vegetation puts forth all its magnificence; her skies, kindling with the magic of summer clouds and glorious sunshine,— no, never need an American look beyond his own country for the sublime and beautiful of natural scenery.

But Europe held forth all the charms of storied and poetical association. There were to be seen the masterpieces of art, the refinements of highly cultivated society, the quaint peculiarities of ancient and local custom. My native country was full of youthful promise: Europe was rich in the accumulated treasures of age. Her very ruins told the history of times gone by, and every moldering stone was a chronicle. I longed to wander over the scenes of renowned achievement; to tread, as it were, in the footsteps of antiquity; to loiter about the ruined castle; to meditate on the falling tower; to escape, in short, from the commonplace realities of the present, and lose myself among the shadowy grandeurs of the past.

I had, beside all this, an earnest desire to see the great men of the earth. We have, it is true, our great men in America: not a city but has an ample share of them. I have mingled among them in my time, and been almost withered by the shade into which they cast me; for there is nothing so baleful to a small man as the shade of a great one, particularly the great man of a city. But I was anxious to see the great men of Europe; for I had read in the works of various philosophers, that all animals degenerated in America, and man among the number. A great man of Europe, thought I, must therefore be as superior to a great man of America as a peak of the Alps to a highland of the Hudson; and in this idea I was confirmed by observing the comparative importance and swelling magnitude of many English travelers among us, who, I was assured, were very little people in their own country. I will visit this land of wonders, thought I, and see the gigantic race from which I am degenerated.

It has been either my good or evil lot to have my roving passion gratified. I have wandered through different countries, and witnessed many of the shifting scenes of life. I cannot say that I have studied them with the eye of a philosopher, but rather with the sauntering gaze with which humble lovers of the picturesque stroll from the window of one print-shop to another; caught sometimes by the delineations of beauty, sometimes by the distortions of caricature, and sometimes by the loveliness of landscape. As it is the fashion for modern tourists to travel pencil in hand, and bring home their portfolios filled with sketches, I am disposed to get up a few for the entertainment of my friends. When, however, I look over the hints and memorandums I have taken down for the purpose, my heart almost fails me at finding how my idle humor has led me aside from the great objects studied by every regular traveler who would make a book. I fear I shall give equal disappointment with an unlucky landscape painter, who had traveled on the Continent, but, follow ing the bent of his vagrant inclination, had sketched in nooks and corners and by-places. His sketch-book was accordingly crowded with cottages and landscapes and obscure ruins; but he had neglected to paint St. Peter's[1] or the Colosseum,[2] the cascade of Terni[3] or the Bay of Naples,[4] and had not a single glacier or volcano in his whole collection.

THE VOYAGE.

> *"Ships, ships, I will descrie you*
> *Amidst the main,*
> *I will come and try you,*
> *What you are protecting,*
> *And projecting,*
> *What's your end and aim.*
> *One goes abroad for merchandise and trading,*
> *Another stays to keep his country from invading,*
> *A third is coming home with rich and wealthy lading,*
> *Hallo! my fancie, whither wilt thou go?"*
>
> OLD POEM.

To an American visiting Europe, the long voyage he has to make is an excellent preparative. The temporary absence of worldly scenes and employments produces a state of mind peculiarly fitted to receive new and vivid impressions. The vast space of waters that separates the hemispheres is like a blank

[1] The Church of St. Peter in Rome is built upon the site of the religious edifice erected in the time of Constantine (306), and consecrated as the "Basilica of St. Peter."

[2] A vast amphitheater in Rome, begun by the Emperor Vespasian, A.D. 72, and dedicated A.D. 80. For nearly five hundred years it was the popular resort of Rome. In the year 555 the whole of the city was overflowed by the Tiber, and the lower part of the Colosseum was then destroyed.

[3] A town of Italy in the province of Perugia, noted for the Falls of Velino, which, for volume and beauty, take a very high place among European waterfalls.

[4] No other place in the world combines within the same compass so much natural beauty with so many objects of interest to the antiquary, the historian, and the geologist, as the Bay of Naples.

page in existence. There is no gradual transition, by which, as in Europe, the features and population of one country blend almost imperceptibly with those of another. From the moment you lose sight of the land you have left, all is vacancy until you step on the opposite shore, and are launched at once into the bustle and novelties of another world.

In traveling by land there is a continuity of scene, and a connected succession of persons and incidents, that carry on the story of life, and lessen the effect of absence and separation. We drag, it is true, "a lengthening chain"[1] at each remove of our pilgrimage; but the chain is unbroken: we can trace it back link by link; and we feel that the last of them still grapples us to home. But a wide sea voyage severs us at once. It makes us conscious of being cast loose from the secure anchorage of settled life, and sent adrift upon a doubtful world. It interposes a gulf, not merely imaginary, but real, between us and our homes,— a gulf subject to tempest and fear and uncertainty, that makes distance palpable, and return precarious.

Such, at least, was the case with myself. As I saw the last blue line of my native land fade away like a cloud in the horizon, it seemed as if I had closed one volume of the world and its concerns, and had time for meditation before I opened another. That land, too, now vanishing from my view, which contained all that was most dear to me in life,— what vicissitudes might occur in it, what changes might take place in me, before I should visit it again! Who can tell, when he sets forth to wander, whither he may be driven by the uncertain currents of existence, or when he may return, or whether it may be ever his lot to revisit the scenes of his childhood?

I said that at sea all is vacancy. I should correct the expres-

[1] Goldsmith's Traveller, line 10. Better explained in the first paragraph of his third letter in Citizen of the World; i.e., " The farther I travel I feel the pain of separation with stronger force: those ties that bind me to my native country and you, are still unbroken. By every move I only drag a greater length of chain."

sion. To one given to day-dreaming, and fond of losing himself
in reveries, a sea voyage is full of subjects for meditation; but
then they are the wonders of the deep and of the air, and rather
tend to abstract the mind from worldly themes. I delighted to
loll over the quarter railing, or climb to the maintop, of a calm
day, and muse for hours together on the tranquil bosom of a summer's sea; to gaze upon the piles of golden clouds just peering
above the horizon, fancy them some fairy realms, and people
them with a creation of my own; to watch the gentle, undulating billows, rolling their silver volumes, as if to die away on those
happy shores.

There was a delicious sensation of mingled security and awe
with which I looked down, from my giddy height, on the monsters of the deep at their uncouth gambols,— shoals of porpoises,
tumbling about the bow of the ship; the grampus, slowly heaving
his huge form above the surface; or the ravenous shark, darting,
like a specter, through the blue waters. My imagination would
conjure up all that I had heard or read of the watery world beneath me,— of the finny herds that roam its fathomless valleys,
of the shapeless monsters that lurk among the very foundations
of the earth, and of those wild phantasms that swell the tales of
fishermen and sailors.

Sometimes a distant sail, gliding along the edge of the ocean,
would be another theme of idle speculation. How interesting
this fragment of a world, hastening to rejoin the great mass of
existence! What a glorious monument of human invention, that
has thus triumphed over wind and wave; has brought the ends
of the world into communion; has established an interchange of
blessings, pouring into the sterile regions of the north all the luxuries of the south; has diffused the light of knowledge and the
charities of cultivated life; and has thus bound together those scattered portions of the human race between which Nature seemed
to have thrown an insurmountable barrier.

We one day descried some shapeless object drifting at a distance. At sea everything that breaks the monotony of the sur-

rounding expanse attracts attention. It proved to be the mast of a ship that must have been completely wrecked; for there were the remains of handkerchiefs, by which some of the crew had fastened themselves to this spar, to prevent their being washed off by the waves. There was no trace by which the name of the ship could be ascertained. The wreck had evidently drifted about for many months. Clusters of shell-fish had fastened about it, and long seaweeds flaunted at its sides. But where, thought I, is the crew? Their struggle has long been over; they have gone down amidst the roar of the tempest; their bones lie whitening among the caverns of the deep. Silence, oblivion, like the waves, have closed over them, and no one can tell the story of their end. What sighs have been wafted after that ship! what prayers offered up at the deserted fireside of home! How often has the mistress, the wife, the mother, pored over the daily news to catch some casual intelligence of this rover of the deep! How has expectation darkened into anxiety, anxiety into dread, and dread into despair! Alas! not one memento shall ever return for love to cherish. All that shall ever be known, is that she sailed from her port, "and was never heard of more."

The sight of this wreck, as usual, gave rise to many dismal anecdotes. This was particularly the case in the evening, when the weather, which had hitherto been fair, began to look wild and threatening, and gave indications of one of those sudden storms that will sometimes break in upon the serenity of a summer voyage. As we sat round the dull light of a lamp in the cabin, that made the gloom more ghastly, every one had his tale of shipwreck and disaster. I was particularly struck with a short one related by the captain.

"As I was once sailing," said he, "in a fine stout ship across the Banks of Newfoundland,[1] one of those heavy fogs that prevail in those parts rendered it impossible for us to see far ahead

---

[1] The shoals to the southeast of the Island of Newfoundland, a great resort for fishermen.

even in the daytime; but at night the weather was so thick that
we could not distinguish any object at twice the length of the
ship. I kept lights at the mast-head, and a constant watch forward to look out for fishing-smacks, which are accustomed to lie
at anchor on the Banks. The wind was blowing a smacking
breeze, and we were going at a great rate through the water.
Suddenly the watch gave the alarm of 'A sail ahead!' It was
scarcely uttered before we were upon her. She was a small
schooner, at anchor, with her broadside toward us. The crew
were all asleep, and had neglected to hoist a light. We struck
her just amidships. The force, the size, and weight of our vessel
bore her down below the waves. We passed over her, and were
hurried on our course. As the crashing wreck was sinking beneath us, I had a glimpse of two or three half-naked wretches
rushing from her cabin. They just started from their beds, to be
swallowed, shrieking, by the waves. I heard their drowning cry
mingling with the wind. The blast that bore it to our ears swept
us out of all further hearing. I shall never forget that cry. It
was some time before we could put the ship about, she was under
such headway. We returned, as nearly as we could guess, to
the place where the smack had anchored. We cruised about for
several hours in the dense fog. We fired signal guns, and listened if we might hear the halloo of any survivors; but all was
silent. We never saw or heard anything of them more."

I confess these stories, for a time, put an end to all my fine
fancies. The storm increased with the night. The sea was
lashed into tremendous confusion. There was a fearful, sullen
sound of rushing waves and broken surges. Deep called unto
deep. At times the black volume of clouds overhead seemed
rent asunder by flashes of lightning that quivered along the
foaming billows, and made the succeeding darkness doubly terrible. The thunders bellowed over the wild waste of waters, and
were echoed and prolonged by the mountain waves. As I saw
the ship staggering and plunging among these roaring caverns, it
seemed miraculous that she regained her balance, or preserved

her buoyancy. Her yards would dip into the water. Her bow was almost buried beneath the waves. Sometimes an impending surge appeared ready to overwhelm her, and nothing but a dexterous movement of the helm preserved her from the shock.

When I retired to my cabin, the awful scene still followed me. The whistling of the wind through the rigging sounded like funereal wailings. The creaking of the masts, the straining and groaning of bulk-heads, as the ship labored in the weltering sea, were frightful. As I heard the waves rushing along the side of the ship, and roaring in my very ear, it seemed as if Death were raging round this floating prison, seeking for his prey. The mere starting of a nail, the yawning of a seam, might give him entrance.

A fine day, however, with a tranquil sea and favoring breeze, soon put all these dismal reflections to flight. It is impossible to resist the gladdening influence of fine weather and fair wind at sea. When the ship is decked out in all her canvas, every sail swelled, and careering gayly over the curling waves, how lofty, how gallant, she appears! How she seems to lord it over the deep! I might fill a volume with the reveries of a sea voyage, — for with me it is almost a continual reverie, — but it is time to get to shore.

It was a fine, sunny morning when the thrilling cry of " Land!" was given from the mast-head. None but those who have experienced it can form an idea of the delicious throng of sensations which rush into an American's bosom when he first comes in sight of Europe. There is a volume of associations with the very name. It is the land of promise, teeming with everything of which his childhood has heard, or on which his studious years have pondered.

From that time until the moment of arrival, it was all feverish excitement. The ships of war, that prowled like guardian giants along the coast; the headlands of Ireland, stretching out into the Channel; the Welsh mountains, towering into the clouds, — all were objects of intense interest. As we sailed up the Mer-

sey,[1] I reconnoitered the shores with a telescope. My eye dwelt
with delight on neat cottages, with their trim shrubberies and
green grass plots. I saw the moldering ruin of an abbey overrun
with ivy, and the taper spire of a village church rising from the
brow of a neighboring hill. All were characteristic of England.

The tide and wind were so favorable that the ship was enabled
to come at once to the pier. It was thronged with people,—
some idle lookers-on, others eager expectants of friends or relatives. I could distinguish the merchant to whom the ship was
consigned. I knew him by his calculating brow and restless air.
His hands were thrust into his pockets. He was whistling
thoughtfully, and walking to and fro, a small space having been
accorded him by the crowd, in deference to his temporary importance. There were repeated cheerings and salutations inter-
changed between the shore and the ship as friends happened to
recognize each other. I particularly noticed one young woman
of humble dress but interesting demeanor. She was leaning forward from among the crowd. Her eye hurried over the ship as
it neared the shore, to catch some wished-for countenance. She
seemed disappointed and agitated, when I heard a faint voice
call her name. It was from a poor sailor who had been ill all
the voyage, and had excited the sympathy of every one on board.
When the weather was fine, his messmates had spread a mattress
for him on deck in the shade; but of late his illness had so
increased, that he had taken to his hammock, and only breathed
a wish that he might see his wife before he died. He had been
helped on deck as we came up the river, and was now leaning
against the shrouds, with a countenance so wasted, so pale, so
ghastly, that it was no wonder even the eye of affection did not
recognize him. But at the sound of his voice, her eye darted on
his features. It read at once a whole volume of sorrow. She
clasped her hands, uttered a faint shriek, and stood wringing
them in silent agony.

[1] A river in the county of Lancaster, England, which opens into a fine
estuary before reaching the sea at Liverpool.

All now was hurry and bustle, — the meetings of acquaint-ances, the greetings of friends, the consultations of men of business. I alone was solitary and idle. I had no friend to meet, no cheering to receive. I stepped upon the land of my forefathers, but felt that I was a stranger in the land.

CHRISTMAS.[1]

" But is old, old, good old Christmas gone? Nothing but the hair of his good, gray, old head and beard left? Well, I will have that, seeing I cannot have more of him." — HUE AND CRY AFTER CHRISTMAS.

> *" A man might then behold*
> *At Christmas, in each hall,*
> *Good fires to curb the cold,*
> *And meat for great and small.*
> *The neighbors were friendly bidden,*
> *And all had welcome true,*
> *The poor from the gates were not chidden,*
> *When this old cap was new."*
>
> OLD SONG.[2]

THERE is nothing in England that exercises a more delight-ful spell over my imagination than the lingerings of the holiday customs and rural games of former times. They recall the pictures my fancy used to draw in the May morning of life, when as yet I only knew the world through books, and believed it to be all that poets had painted it; and they bring with them the flavor of those honest days of yore, in which, perhaps, with equal fallacy, I am apt to think the world was more homebred, social, and joyous than at present. I regret to say that they are daily growing more and more faint, being gradually worn away

[1] Christ and Mass (Anglo-Saxon *Maessa,* "a holy day or feast"), the Christian festival of the Nativity. The festival properly begins on the evening of Dec. 24, and lasts until Epiphany, Jan. 6, the whole being termed "Christmas-tide." Dec. 25, however, is the day more specifically observed.

[2] From Guild Hall Giants, by Thomas Hood, a famous English humorist and popular author (born in London, 1798; died, 1845).

by time, but still more obliterated by modern fashion. They resemble those picturesque morsels of Gothic architecture which
we see crumbling in various parts of the country, partly dilapi-
dated by the waste of ages, and partly lost in the additions and
alterations of latter days. Poetry, however, clings with cherishing fondness about the rural game and holiday revel, from which
it has derived so many of its themes, — as the ivy winds its rich
foliage about the Gothic arch and moldering tower, gratefully
repaying their support by clasping together their tottering remains, and, as it were, embalming them in verdure.

Of all the old festivals, however, that of Christmas awakens
the strongest and most heartfelt associations. There is a tone
of solemn and sacred feeling that blends with our conviviality,
and lifts the spirit to a state of hallowed and elevated enjoyment.
The services of the church about this season are extremely tender
and inspiring. They dwell on the beautiful story of the origin of
our faith, and the pastoral scenes that accompanied its announcement. They gradually increase in fervor and pathos during the
season of Advent,[1] until they break forth in full jubilee on the
morning that brought peace and good will to men.[2] I do not
know a grander effect of music on the moral feelings than to
hear the full choir and the pealing organ performing a Christmas
anthem in a cathedral, and filling every part of the vast pile with
triumphant harmony.

It is a beautiful arrangement, also, derived from days of yore,
that this festival, which commemorates the announcement of the
religion of peace and love, has been made the season for gathering together of family connections, and drawing closer again those

---

[1] The season of moral and religious preparation, between St. Andrew's
Day (Nov. 30) and Christmas. Its observance dates from the fourth century, and from the sixth century it has been recognized as the beginning of
the ecclesiastical year. At one time it was observed as strictly as Lent.
Advent fasting is now confined to the week in which Ember Day (Dec. 13)
occurs.

[2] No war was declared, and no capital executions were permitted to take
place, during this season of good will.

bands of kindred hearts which the cares and pleasures and sorrows of the world are continually operating to cast loose; of
calling back the children of a family, who have launched forth in
life, and wandered widely asunder, once more to assemble about
the paternal hearth, that rallying-place of the affections, there to
grow young and loving again among the endearing mementos of
childhood.

There is something in the very season of the year that gives a
charm to the festivity of Christmas. At other times we derive a
great portion of our pleasures from the mere beauties of nature.
Our feelings sally forth and dissipate themselves over the sunny
landscape, and we "live abroad and everywhere." The song of
the bird; the murmur of the stream; the breathing fragrance of
spring; the soft voluptuousness of summer; the golden pomp of
autumn; earth, with its mantle of refreshing green; and heaven,
with its deep, delicious blue and its cloudy magnificence, — all fill
us with mute but exquisite delight, and we revel in the luxury of
mere sensation. But in the depth of winter, when Nature lies
despoiled of every charm and wrapped in her shroud of sheeted
snow, we turn for our gratifications to moral sources. The dreariness and desolation of the landscape, the short, gloomy days and
darksome nights, while they circumscribe our wanderings, shut in
our feelings also from rambling abroad, and make us more keenly
disposed for the pleasures of the social circle. Our thoughts are
more concentrated, our friendly sympathies more aroused. We
feel more sensibly the charm of each other's society, and are
brought more closely together by dependence on each other for
enjoyment. Heart calleth unto heart; and we draw our pleasures from the deep wells of living kindness, which lie in the quiet
recesses of our bosoms, and which, when resorted to, furnish
forth the pure element of domestic felicity.

The pitchy gloom without makes the heart dilate on entering the room filled with the glow and warmth of the evening
fire. The ruddy blaze diffuses an artificial summer and sunshine
through the room, and lights up each countenance into a kindlier

welcome. Where does the honest face of hospitality expand into a broader and more cordial smile, where is the shy glance of love more sweetly eloquent, than by the winter fireside? and as the hollow blast of wintry wind rushes through the hall, claps the distant door, whistles about the casement, and rumbles down the chimney, what can be more grateful than that feeling of sober and sheltered security with which we look round upon the comfortable chamber and the scene of domestic hilarity?

The English, from the great prevalence of rural habits throughout every class of society, have always been fond of those festivals and holidays which agreeably interrupt the stillness of country life, and they were in former days particularly observant of the religious and social rites of Christmas.[1] It is inspiring to read even the dry details which some antiquaries have given of the quaint humors, the burlesque pageants, the complete abandonment to mirth and good-fellowship, with which this festival was celebrated. It seemed to throw open every door, and unlock every heart. It brought the peasant and the peer together, and blended all ranks in one warm generous flow of joy and kindness.[2] The old halls of castles and manor-houses resounded with the harp and the Christmas carol,[3] and their ample boards groaned under the weight of hospitality. Even the poorest cottage welcomed the festive season with green decorations of bay[4]

[1] Christmas Day, in the primitive Church, was always observed as the sabbath day, and, like that, preceded by an eve or vigil: hence our present Christmas Eve.

[2] In farmhouses in the north of England the servants used to lay a large knotty block for their Christmas fire, and during the time it lasted they were entitled by custom to ale at their meals.

[3] The well-known hymn, "Gloria in Excelsis," sung by the angels to the shepherds at our Lord's nativity, was the earliest Christmas carol. We next hear of one sung in the thirteenth century. It is in the British Museum, and written in Anglo-Norman.

[4] Since the days of the ancient Romans, this tree, a species of laurel, the aromatic leaves of which are often found packed with figs, has at all times been dedicated to all purposes of joyous commemoration; and its branches have been used as the emblems of peace, victory, and joy.

and holly.[1] The cheerful fire glanced its rays through the lattice, inviting the passenger to raise the latch, and join the gossip knot huddled round the hearth, beguiling the long evening with legendary jokes and oft-told Christmas tales.

One of the least pleasing effects of modern refinement is the havoc it has made among the hearty old holiday customs. It has completely taken off the sharp touchings and spirited reliefs of these embellishments of life, and has worn down society into a more smooth and polished, but certainly a less characteristic surface. Many of the games and ceremonials of Christmas have entirely disappeared, and, like the sherris sack of old Falstaff,[2] are become matters of speculation and dispute among commentators. They flourished in times full of spirit and lustihood, when men enjoyed life roughly, but heartily and vigorously, — times wild and picturesque, which have furnished poetry with its richest materials, and the drama with its most attractive variety of characters and manners. The world has become more worldly. There is more of dissipation, and less of enjoyment. Pleasure has expanded into a broader but a shallower stream, and has forsaken many of those deep and quiet channels where it flowed sweetly through the calm bosom of domestic life. Society has acquired a more enlightened and elegant tone; but it has lost many of its strong local peculiarities, its home-bred feelings, its honest fireside delights. The traditionary customs of golden-hearted antiquity, its feudal hospitalities, and lordly wassailings, have passed away with the baronial castles and stately manor-houses in which they were celebrated. They comported with the shadowy hall, the great oaken gallery, and the tapestried parlor, but are unfitted for the light, showy saloons and gay drawing-rooms of the modern villa.[3]

[1] A plant of the genus *Ilex*. The common holly grows from twenty to thirty feet in height. It is especially used about Christmas time to decorate the inside of houses and churches, — a relic, it is thought, of Druidism.

[2] Second Henry IV., act iv. sc. 3.

[3] In 1589 an order was issued to the gentlemen of Norfolk and Suffolk, commanding them " to depart from London before Christmas, and to repair to their country homes, there to keep hospitality amongst their neighbors."

Shorn, however, as it is, of its ancient and festive honors, Christmas is still a period of delightful excitement in England. It is gratifying to see that home feeling completely aroused which holds so powerful a place in every English bosom. The preparations making on every side for the social board that is again to unite friends and kindred; the presents[1] of good cheer passing and repassing, those tokens of regard, and quickeners of kind feelings; the evergreens distributed about houses and churches, emblems of peace and gladness,—all these have the most pleasing effect in producing fond associations, and kindling benevolent sympathies. Even the sound of the waits,[2] rude as may be their minstrelsy, breaks upon the mid-watches of a winter night with the effect of perfect harmony. As I have been awakened by them in that still and solemn hour "when deep sleep falleth upon man," I have listened with a hushed delight, and, connecting them with the sacred and joyous occasion, have almost fancied them into another celestial choir,[3] announcing peace and good will to mankind. How delightfully the imagination, when wrought upon by these moral influences, turns everything to melody and beauty! The very crowing of the cock, heard sometimes in the profound repose of the country, "telling the night watches to his feathery dames," was thought by the common people to announce the approach of this sacred festival.

> " Some say that ever 'gainst that season comes
> Wherein our Saviour's birth is celebrated,
> The bird of dawning singeth all night long:
> And then, they say, no spirit dare stir abroad;
> The nights are wholesome; then no planets strike,
> No fairy takes, no witch hath power to charm,
> So hallowed and so gracious is the time."[4]

---

[1] The practice of giving presents at Christmas was undoubtedly founded on the Pagan custom of New-Year's gifts, with which in these times it is blended.

[2] Or wayte, originally a kind of night-watchman who sounded the hours of his watch, and guarded the streets; later, a musician who sang out of doors at Christmas time, going from house to house.

[3] Luke ii. 13, 14.   [4] Hamlet, act i. sc. i.

Amidst the general call to happiness, the bustle of the spirits, and stir of the affections, which prevail at this period, what bosom can remain insensible? It is, indeed, the season of regenerated feeling, — the season for kindling, not merely the fire of hospitality in the hall, but the genial flame of charity in the heart. The scene of early love again rises green to memory beyond the sterile waste of years; and the idea of home, fraught with the fragrance of home-dwelling joys, reanimates the drooping spirit, as the Arabian breeze will sometimes waft the freshness of the distant fields to the weary pilgrim of the desert.

Stranger and sojourner as I am in the land, — though for me no social hearth may blaze, no hospitable roof throw open its doors, nor the warm grasp of friendship welcome me at the threshold, — yet I feel the influence of the season beaming into my soul from the happy looks of those around me. Surely happiness is reflective, like the light of heaven; and every countenance, bright with smiles, and glowing with innocent enjoyment, is a mirror transmitting to others the rays of a supreme and ever-shining benevolence. He who can turn churlishly away from contemplating the felicity of his fellow-beings, and can sit down darkling and repining in his loneliness when all around is joyful, may have his moments of strong excitement and selfish gratification, but he wants the genial and social sympathies which constitute the charm of a merry Christmas.

THE STAGECOACH.

" Omne benè
Sine pœnâ
Tempus est ludendi
Venit hora
Absque morâ
Libros deponendi." [1]

OLD HOLIDAY SCHOOL SONG.

IN the preceding paper I have made some general observations on the Christmas festivities of England, and am tempted to illustrate them by some anecdotes of a Christmas passed in the country; in perusing which I would most courteously invite my reader to lay aside the austerity of wisdom, and to put on that genuine holiday spirit which is tolerant of folly, and anxious only for amusement.

In the course of a December tour in Yorkshire,[2] I rode for a long distance in one of the public coaches on the day preceding Christmas. The coach was crowded, both inside and out, with passengers, who, by their talk, seemed principally bound to the mansions of relations or friends, to eat the Christmas dinner. It was loaded also with hampers of game, and baskets and boxes of delicacies; and hares hung dangling their long ears about the coachman's box, presents from distant friends for the impending feast. I had three fine rosy-cheeked schoolboys for my fellow-passengers inside, full of the buxom health and manly spirit which I have observed in the children of this country. They were returning home for the holidays in high glee, and promising themselves a world of enjoyment. It was delightful to hear the

---

1 Free translation:—

" There's a time for hard playing,
With nothing to fear.
Drop books without delaying—
The hour is here."

2 A northern county of England, famed for the beauty of its river scenery, in which respect it is scarcely surpassed by Scotland.

gigantic plans of pleasure of the little rogues, and the impractica-
ble feats they were to perform during their six-weeks' emancipation
from the abhorred thraldom of book, birch, and pedagogue. They
were full of the anticipations of the meeting with the family and
household, down to the very cat and dog, and of the joy they
were to give their little sisters by the presents with which their
pockets were crammed; but the meeting to which they seemed
to look forward with the greatest impatience was with Bantam,
which I found to be a pony, and, according to their talk, possessed of more virtues than any steed since the days of Buceph-
alus.[1] How he could trot! How he could run! And then such
leaps as he would take! There was not a hedge in the whole
country that he could not clear.

They were under the particular guardianship of the coachman,
to whom, whenever an opportunity presented, they addressed a
host of questions, and pronounced him one of the best fellows in
the whole world.   Indeed, I could not but notice the more than
ordinary air of bustle and importance of the coachman, who wore
his hat a little on one side, and had a large bunch of Christmas
greens stuck in the buttonhole of his coat.   He is always a personage full of mighty care and business, but he is particularly so
during this season, having so many commissions to execute in
consequence of the great interchange of presents.   And here,
perhaps, it may not be unacceptable to my untraveled readers to
have a sketch that may serve as a general representation of this
very numerous and important class of functionaries, who have a
dress, a manner, a language, an air, peculiar to themselves, and
prevalent throughout the fraternity; so that, wherever an English
stagecoach-man may be seen, he cannot be mistaken for one of
any other craft or mystery.

He has commonly a broad, full face, curiously mottled with
red, as if the blood had been forced by hard feeding into every
vessel of the skin.   He is swelled into jolly dimensions by frequent potations of malt liquors; and his bulk is still further in-

---

[1] The horse of Alexander the Great.

creased by a multiplicity of coats, in which he is buried like a cauliflower, the upper one reaching to his heels. He wears a broad-brimmed, low-crowned hat; a huge roll of colored handkerchief about his neck, knowingly knotted, and tucked in at the bosom; and has in summer time a large bouquet of flowers in his buttonhole, — the present, most probably, of some enamored country lass. His waistcoat is commonly of some bright color, striped, and his small-clothes extend far below the knees, to meet a pair of jockey boots which reach about halfway up his legs.

All this costume is maintained with much precision. He has a pride in having his clothes of excellent materials; and, notwithstanding the seeming grossness of his appearance, there is still discernible that neatness and propriety of person which is almost inherent in an Englishman. He enjoys great consequence and consideration along the road; has frequent conferences with the village housewives, who look upon him as a man of great trust and dependence; and he seems to have a good understanding with every bright-eyed country lass. The moment he arrives where the horses are to be changed, he throws down the reins with something of an air, and abandons the cattle to the care of the hostler, his duty being merely to drive them from one stage to another. When off the box,[1] his hands are thrust in the pockets of his great-coat, and he rolls about the inn yard with an air of the most absolute lordliness. Here he is generally surrounded by an admiring throng of hostlers, stable-boys, shoeblacks, and those nameless hangers-on that infest inns and taverns, and run errands, and do all kind of odd jobs, for the privilege of battening on the drippings of the kitchen and the leakage of the tap-room. These all look up to him as to an oracle; treasure up his cant phrases; echo his opinions about horses and other topics of jockey lore; and, above all, endeavor to imitate his air and carriage. Every ragamuffin that has a coat to his back, thrusts his hands in the pockets, rolls in his gait, talks slang, and is an embryo coachey.[2]

---

[1] The place beneath the driver's seat on a coach: hence the seat itself.
[2] Coachman; stage-driver.

Perhaps it might be owing to the pleasing serenity that reigned in my own mind, that 1 fancied I saw cheerfulness in every countenance throughout the journey. A stagecoach, however, carries animation always with it, and puts the world in motion as it whirls along. The horn, sounded at the entrance of a village, produces a general bustle. Some hasten forth to meet friends; some, with bundles and bandboxes, to secure places, and, in the hurry of the moment, can hardly take leave of the group that accompanies them. In the mean time the coachman has a world of small commissions to execute: sometimes he delivers a hare or pheasant; sometimes jerks a small parcel or newspaper to the door of a public house; and sometimes, with knowing leer and words of sly import, hands to some half-blushing, half-laughing housemaid an odd-shaped billet-doux [1] from some rustic admirer. As the coach rattles through the village, every one runs to the window, and you have glances on every side of fresh country faces and blooming giggling girls. At the corners are assembled juntos [2] of village idlers and wise men, who take their stations there for the important purpose of seeing company pass; but the sagest knot is generally at the blacksmith's, to whom the passing of the coach is an event fruitful of much speculation. The smith, with the horse's heel in his lap, pauses as the vehicle whirls by; the cyclops [3] round the anvil suspend their ringing hammers, and suffer the iron to grow cool; and the sooty specter, in brown paper cap, laboring at the bellows, leans on the handle for a moment, and permits the asthmatic engine to heave a long-drawn sigh, while he glares through the murky smoke and sulphureous gleams of the smithy.

---

[1] French, *billet* ("small letter") and *doux* ("sweet"): hence a love-letter.

[2] Originally private councils; here merely in the sense of gossiping groups.

[3] The cyclops, according to Greek mythology and story, were a race of stalwart giants with one eye in their foreheads: hence their name (Greek *ku-klopes, kuklos,* "a circle;" and *ops,* "eye"), the round-eyed. They forged the thunderbolts of Zeus, the trident of Poseidon, and the helmet of Pluto. The allusion is to their size and strength as gigantic blacksmiths.

Perhaps the impending holiday might have given a more than usual animation to the country, for it seemed to me as if everybody was in good looks and good spirits. Game, poultry, and other luxuries of the table, were in brisk circulation in the villages. The grocers', butchers', and fruiterers' shops were thronged with customers. The housewives were stirring briskly about, putting their dwellings in order; and the glossy branches of holly, with their bright-red berries, began to appear at the windows. The scene brought to mind an old writer's account of Christmas preparations: "Now capons and hens, besides turkeys, geese, and ducks, with beef and mutton — must all die — for in twelve days a multitude of people will not be fed with a little. Now plums and spice, sugar and honey, square it among pies and broth. Now or never must music be in tune, for the youth must dance and sing to get them a heat, while the aged sit by the fire. The country maid leaves half her market, and must be sent again, if she forgets a pack of cards[1] on Christmas Eve. Great is the contention of holly and ivy, whether master or dame wears the breeches. Dice and cards benefit the butler; and if the cook do not lack wit, he will sweetly lick his fingers."[2]

I was roused from this fit of luxurious meditation by a shout from my little traveling companions. They had been looking out of the coach windows for the last few miles, recognizing every tree and cottage as they approached home, and now there was a general burst of joy. "There's John, and there's old Carlo, and there's Bantam!" cried the happy little rogues, clapping their hands.

At the end of a lane there was an old, sober-looking servant

---

[1] Cards furnished one of the great resources at this season of long evenings and indoor amusements, as they appear also to have formed an express feature of the Christmas entertainments of all ranks of people in old times. We are told that the squire in Queen Anne's time "never played cards but at Christmas, when the family pack was produced from the mantelpiece."

[2] Stevenson, in Twelve Months (1661).

in livery, waiting for them.   He was accompanied by a superannuated pointer, and by the redoubtable Bantam,—a little old rat of a pony, with a shaggy mane, and long, rusty tail, who stood dozing quietly by the roadside, little dreaming of the bustling times that awaited him.

I was pleased to see the fondness with which the little fellows leaped about the steady old footman, and hugged the pointer, who wriggled his whole body for joy.   But Bantam was the great object of interest.   All wanted to mount at once; and it was with some difficulty that John arranged that they should ride by turns, and the eldest should ride first.

Off they set at last,—one on the pony, with the dog bounding and barking before him; and the others holding John's hands, both talking at once, and overpowering him with questions about home, and with school anecdotes.   I looked after them with a feeling in which I do not know whether pleasure or melancholy predominated; for I was reminded of those days when, like them, I had neither known care nor sorrow, and a holiday was the summit of earthly felicity.   We stopped a few moments afterwards to water the horses, and, on resuming our route, a turn of the road brought us in sight of a neat country seat.   I could just distinguish the forms of a lady and two young girls in the portico; and I saw my little comrades, with Bantam, Carlo, and old John, trooping along the carriage road.   I leaned out of the coach window, in hopes of witnessing the happy meeting, but a grove of trees shut it from my sight.

In the evening we reached a village where I had determined to pass the night.   As we drove into the great gateway of the inn, I saw on one side the light of a rousing kitchen fire beaming through a window.   I entered, and admired, for the hundredth time, that picture of convenience, neatness, and broad, honest enjoyment, the kitchen of an English inn.   It was of spacious dimensions, hung round with copper and tin vessels highly polished, and decorated here and there with a Christmas green. Hams, tongues, and flitches of bacon were suspended from the

ceiling; a smoke-jack[1] made its ceaseless clanking beside the
fireplace; and a clock ticked in one corner. A well-scoured
deal table extended along one side of the kitchen, with a cold
round of beef and other hearty viands upon it, over which two
foaming tankards of ale seemed mounting guard. Travelers of
inferior order were preparing to attack this stout repast, while
others sat smoking and gossiping over their ale on two high-
backed oaken settles[2] beside the fire. Trim housemaids were
hurrying backwards and forwards under the directions of a fresh
bustling landlady, but still seizing an occasional moment to ex
change a flippant word, and have a rallying laugh, with the group
round the fire. The scene completely realized Poor Robin's[3]
humble idea of the comforts of mid-winter:—

> " Now trees their leafy hats do bare
> To reverence Winter's silver hair,
> A handsome hostess, merry host,
> A pot of ale, and now a toast,
> Tobacco and a good coal fire,
> Are things this season doth require."

I had not been long at the inn when a post-chaise drove up to
the door. A young gentleman stepped out, and by the light of
the lamps I caught a glimpse of a countenance which I thought
I knew. I moved forward to get a nearer view, when his eye
caught mine. I was not mistaken: it was Frank Bracebridge,
a sprightly, good-humored young fellow, with whom I had once
traveled on the Continent. Our meeting was extremely cordial,
for the countenance of an old fellow-traveler always brings up
the recollection of a thousand pleasant scenes, odd adventures,
and excellent jokes. To discuss all these in a transient interview

---

[1] A machine used to rotate a roasting-spit, and operated by the current of
rising air in a chimney.

[2] Benches.

[3] " Poor Robin " was the pseudonym of Robert Herrick, the poet, under
which he issued a series of almanacs (begun in 1661). The quotation is from
the almanac for 1684.

at an inn was impossible ; and finding that I was not pressed for time, and was merely making a tour of observation, he insisted that I should give him a day or two at his father's country seat, to which he was going to pass the holidays, and which lay at a few miles' distance. "It is better than eating a solitary Christmas dinner at an inn," said he, " and I can assure you of a hearty welcome in something of the old-fashioned style." His reasoning was cogent, and I must confess the preparation I had seen for universal festivity and social enjoyment had made me feel a little impatient of my loneliness. I closed, therefore, at once, with his invitation : the chaise drove up to the door, and in a few moments I was on my way to the family mansion of the Bracebridges.

CHRISTMAS EVE.

> " *Saint Francis and Saint Benedight*
> *Blesse this house from wicked wight ;*
> *From the night-mare and the goblin,*
> *That is hight good fellow Robin ;*
> *Keep it from all evil spirits,*
> *Fairies, weazles, rats, and ferrets :*
> *From curfew-time*
> *To the next prime.*"
>
> CARTWRIGHT.[1]

IT was a brilliant moonlight night, but extremely cold. Our chaise whirled rapidly over the frozen ground. The post-boy smacked his whip incessantly, and a part of the time his horses were on a gallop. " He knows where he is going," said my companion, laughing, "and is eager to arrive in time for some of the merriment and good cheer of the servants' hall.[2] My father, you

[1] William Cartwright (1611–43), an English poet and clergyman, was very popular in his time, especially about Oxford, where he was educated, and where he afterwards preached.

[2] The servants had enlarged privileges during this season, not only by custom, but by positive enactment ; and certain games, which at other periods they were prohibited from engaging in, were allowed at Christmas time.

must know, is a bigoted devotee of the old school, and prides
himself upon keeping up something of old English hospitality.
He is a tolerable specimen of what you will rarely meet with
nowadays in its purity, — the old English country gentleman; for
our men of fortune spend so much of their time in town, and
fashion is carried so much into the country, that the strong, rich
peculiarities of ancient rural life are almost polished away.   My
father, however, from early years, took honest Peacham [1] for his
text-book, instead of Chesterfield.[2]   He determined in his own
mind that there was no condition more truly honorable and enviable than that of a country gentleman on his paternal lands,
and therefore passes the whole of his time on his estate.   He is
a strenuous advocate for the revival of the old rural games and
holiday observances, and is deeply read in the writers, ancient
and modern, who have treated on the subject.   Indeed, his favorite range of reading is among the authors who flourished at
least two centuries since, who, he insists, wrote and thought more
like true Englishmen than any of their successors.   He even re-
grets sometimes that he had not been born a few centuries earlier, when England was itself, and had its peculiar manners and
customs.   As he lives at some distance from the main road, in
rather a lonely part of the country, without any rival gentry near
him, he has that most enviable of all blessings to an Englishman,
an opportunity of indulging the bent of his own humor without
molestation.   Being representative of the oldest family in the
neighborhood, and a great part of the peasantry being his tenants, he is much looked up to, and, in general, is known simply
by the appellation of 'The Squire,' — a title which has been accorded to the head of the family since time immemorial.   I think
it best to give you these hints about my worthy old father, to

---

[1] Henry Peacham (born in Hertfordshire, England, in the sixteenth century) was the author of The Complete Gentleman (1622).

[2] Chesterfield (Philip Dormer Stanhope) was an English courtier, orator,
and wit, renowned as a model of politeness, and criterion of taste.   He was
born in London in 1694.

prepare you for any little eccentricities that might otherwise appear absurd."

We had passed for some time along the wall of a park, and at length the chaise stopped at the gate. It was in a heavy, magnificent old style, of iron bars, fancifully wrought at top into flourishes and flowers. The huge, square columns that supported the gate were surmounted by the family crest. Close adjoining was the porter's lodge, sheltered under dark fir-trees, and almost buried in shrubbery.

The post-boy rang a large porter's bell, which resounded through the still, frosty air, and was answered by the distant barking of dogs, with which the mansion-house seemed garrisoned. An old woman immediately appeared at the gate. As the moonlight fell strongly upon her, I had a full view of a little primitive dame, dressed very much in antique taste, with a neat kerchief and stomacher,[1] and her silver hair peeping from under a cap of snowy whiteness. She came courtesying forth, with many expressions of simple joy at seeing her young master. Her husband, it seemed, was up at the house keeping Christmas Eve in the servants' hall. They could not do without him, as he was the best hand at a song and story in the household.

My friend proposed that we should alight, and walk through the park to the hall, which was at no great distance, while the chaise should follow on. Our road wound through a noble avenue of trees, among the naked branches of which the moon glittered, as she rolled through the deep vault of a cloudless sky. The lawn beyond was sheeted with a slight covering of snow, which here and there sparkled as the moonbeams caught a frosty crystal; and at a distance might be seen a thin, transparent vapor, stealing up from the low grounds, and threatening gradually to shroud the landscape.

My companion looked round him with transport. "How often," said he, "have I scampered up this avenue, on returning

[1] The portion of a dress forming, generally, the lower part of the bodice, extending down in front into the skirt, and usually overlapping it.

home on school vacations! How often have I played under these
trees when a boy! I feel a degree of filial reverence for them,
as we look up to those who have cherished us in childhood. My
father was always scrupulous in exacting our holidays, and having us around him on family festivals. He used to direct and
superintend our games with the strictness that some parents do
the studies of their children. He was very particular that we
should play the old English games according to their original
form, and consulted old books for precedent and authority for
every 'merrie disport;' yet I assure you there never was pedantry
so delightful. It was the policy of the good old gentleman to
make his children feel that home was the happiest place in the
world; and I value this delicious home feeling as one of the
choicest gifts a parent could bestow."

We were interrupted by the clamor of a troop of dogs of all
sorts and sizes, — "mongrel, puppy, whelp, and hound, and curs
of low degree," — that, disturbed by the ringing of the porter's
bell and the rattling of the chaise, came bounding, open-mouthed,
across the lawn.

> "The little dogs and all,
> Tray, Blanch, and Sweet-heart, see, they bark at me."[1]

cried Bracebridge, laughing. At the sound of his voice, the bark
was changed into a yelp of delight, and in a moment he was surrounded and almost overpowered by the caresses of the faithful
animals.

We had now come in full view of the old family mansion,
partly thrown in deep shadow, and partly lit up by the cold
moonshine. It was an irregular building of some magnitude,
and seemed to be of the architecture of different periods. One
wing was evidently very ancient, with heavy stone-shafted bow-
windows jutting out and overrun with ivy, from among the foliage of which the small, diamond-shaped panes of glass glittered
with the moonbeams. The rest of the house was in the French

[1] King Lear, act iii. sc. 6.

taste of Charles II.'s [1] time, having been repaired and altered, as
my friend told me, by one of his ancestors, who returned with
that monarch at the Restoration. [2]   The grounds about the house
were laid out in the old formal manner of artificial flower-beds,
clipped shrubberies, raised terraces, and heavy stone balustrades,
ornamented with urns, a leaden statue or two, and a jet of water.
The old gentleman, I was told, was extremely careful to preserve
this obsolete finery in all its original state.   He admired this
fashion in gardening : it had an air of magnificence, was courtly
and noble, and befitting good old family style.   The boasted imitation of nature in modern gardening had sprung up with modern
republican notions, but did not suit a monarchical government :
it smacked of the leveling system.   I could not help smiling at
this introduction of politics into gardening, though I expressed
some apprehension that I should find the old gentleman rather
intolerant in his creed.   Frank assured me, however, that it was
almost the only instance in which he had ever heard his father
meddle with politics ; and he believed he had got this notion
from a member of Parliament who once passed a few weeks with
him.   The Squire was glad of any argument to defend his clipped
yew-trees and formal terraces, which had been occasionally attacked by modern landscape-gardeners.

As we approached the house, we heard the sound of music,
and now and then a burst of laughter, from one end of the building.   This, Bracebridge said, must proceed from the servants'
hall, where a great deal of revelry was permitted, and even encouraged by the Squire, throughout the twelve days [3] of Christmas, provided every thing was done conformably to ancient

[1] Charles II. (born, 1630) was proclaimed king by the Scottish Parliament in 1649.   He landed in Scotland in 1650, and was crowned the following year.   He marched into England against Cromwell, but was defeated at
Worcester in 1651.

[2] In English history, the reëstablishing of the monarchy with Charles II.
in 1660, and the period of his reign.

[3] Referring to the period between Christmas and Epiphany, or from Dec.
25 to Jan. 6.

usage.   Here were kept up the old games of hoodman blind,
shoe the wild mare, hot cockles, steal the white loaf, bob-apple,
and snap-dragon.   The Yule clog[1] and Christmas candle were
regularly burnt; and the mistletoe, with its white berries, hung
up, to the imminent peril of all the pretty house-maids.[2]

So intent were the servants upon their sports, that we had to
ring repeatedly before we could make ourselves heard.   On our
arrival being announced, the Squire came out to receive us, accompanied by his two other sons, — one a young officer in the
army, home on leave of absence; the other an Oxonian, just
from the university.   The Squire was a fine, healthy-looking old
gentleman, with silver hair curling lightly round an open, florid
countenance, in which a physiognomist, with the advantage, like
myself, of a previous hint or two, might discover a singular mixture of whim and benevolence.

[1] IRVING'S NOTE.— The Yule clog is a great log of wood, sometimes the
root of a tree, brought into the house with great ceremony on Christmas Eve,
laid in the fireplace, and lighted with the brand of last year's clog.   While
it lasted, there was great drinking, singing, and telling of tales.   Sometimes
it was accompanied by Christmas candles, but in the cottages the only light
was from the ruddy blaze of the great wood fire.   The Yule clog was to burn
all night: if it went out, it was considered a sign of ill luck.   Herrick mentions it in one of his songs: —

> "Come, bring with a noise,
>   My merrie, merrie boyes,
> The Christmas log to the firing;
>   While my good dame, she
>   Bids ye all be free,
> And drink to your hearts desiring."

The Yule clog is still burnt in many farmhouses and kitchens in England,
particularly in the north, and there are several superstitions connected with
it among the peasantry.   If a squinting person come to the house while it is
burning, or a person barefooted, it is considered an ill omen.   The brand
remaining from the Yule clog is carefully put away to light the next year's
Christmas fire.

[2] IRVING'S NOTE.— The mistletoe is still hung up in farmhouses and
kitchens at Christmas, and the young men have the privilege of kissing the
girls under it, plucking each time a berry from the bush.   When the berries
are all plucked, the privilege ceases.

The family meeting was warm and affectionate. As the evening was far advanced, the Squire would not permit us to change our traveling dresses, but ushered us at once to the company, which was assembled in a large, old-fashioned hall. It was composed of different branches of a numerous family connection, where there were the usual proportions of old uncles and aunts, comfortable married dames, superannuated spinsters, blooming country cousins, half-fledged striplings, and bright-eyed boarding-school hoidens. They were variously occupied,— some at a round game of cards; others conversing around the fireplace; at one end of the hall was a group of the young folks, some nearly grown up, others of a more tender and budding age, fully engrossed by a merry game; and a profusion of wooden horses, penny trumpets, and tattered dolls about the floor, showed traces of a troop of little fairy beings, who, having frolicked through a happy day, had been carried off to slumber through a peaceful night.

While the mutual greetings were going on between young Bracebridge and his relatives, I had time to scan the apartment. I have called it a hall, for so it had certainly been in old times, and the Squire had evidently endeavored to restore it to something of its primitive state. Over the heavy projecting fireplace was suspended a picture of a warrior in armor, standing by a white horse; and on the opposite wall hung a helmet, buckler, and lance. At one end an enormous pair of antlers were inserted in the wall, the branches serving as hooks on which to suspend hats, whips, and spurs; and in the corners of the apartment were fowling-pieces, fishing-rods, and other sporting implements. The furniture was of the cumbrous workmanship of former days, though some articles of modern convenience had been added, and the oaken floor had been carpeted; so that the whole presented an odd mixture of parlor and hall.

The grate had been removed from the wide, overwhelming fireplace, to make way for a fire of wood, in the midst of which was an enormous log, glowing and blazing, and sending forth a vast volume of light and heat: this I understood was the Yule clog, which the Squire was particular in having brought in and illumined on a Christmas Eve, according to ancient custom.

It was really delightful to see the old Squire seated in his hereditary elbow chair, by the hospitable fireside of his ancestors, and looking around him like the sun of a system, beaming warmth and gladness to every heart. Even the very dog that lay stretched at his feet, as he lazily shifted his position and yawned, would look fondly up in his master's face, wag his tail against the floor, and stretch himself again to sleep, confident of kindness and protection. There is an emanation from the heart in genuine hospitality which cannot be described, but is immediately felt, and puts the stranger at once at his ease. I had not been seated many minutes by the comfortable hearth of the worthy old cavalier, before I found myself as much at home as if I had been one of the family.

Supper was announced shortly after our arrival. It was served up in a spacious oaken chamber, the panels of which shone with wax, and around which were several family portraits decorated with holly and ivy.[1] Beside the accustomed lights, two great wax tapers, called Christmas candles,[2] wreathed with greens, were placed on a highly polished beaufet among the family plate. The table was abundantly spread with substantial fare; but the Squire made his supper of frumenty,—a dish made of wheat 'cakes boiled in milk, with rich spices, being a standing dish in old times for Christmas Eve.

I was happy to find my old friend, minced pie,[3] in the retinue

[1] Ivy was used not only as a vintner's sign, but also among the evergreens at funerals.

[2] Christmas was called the "Feast of Lights" in the Western or Latin Church, because they used many lights or candles at the feast; or, rather, because Christ, the Light of all lights, that true Light, came into the world: hence the Christmas candle.

[3] By some it has been supposed, from the Oriental ingredients which enter into its composition, to have a reference to the offerings made by the Wise Men of the East; and it was anciently the custom to make these pies of an

of the feast; and finding him to be perfectly orthodox, and that I need not be ashamed of my predilection, I greeted him with all the warmth wherewith we usually greet an old and very genteel acquaintance.

The mirth of the company was greatly promoted by the humors of an eccentric personage whom Mr. Bracebridge always addressed with the quaint appellation of Master Simon. He was a tight, brisk little man, with the air of an arrant old bachelor. His nose was shaped like the bill of a parrot; his face, slightly pitted with the small-pox, with a dry, perpetual bloom on it, like a frost-bitten leaf in autumn. He had an eye of great quickness and vivacity, with a drollery and lurking waggery of expression that was irresistible. He was evidently the wit of the family, dealing very much in sly jokes and innuendoes with the ladies, and making infinite merriment by harpings upon old themes; which, unfortunately, my ignorance of the family chronicles did not permit me to enjoy. It seemed to be his great delight during supper to keep a young girl next him in a continual agony of stifled laughter, in spite of her awe of the reproving looks of her mother, who sat opposite. Indeed, he was the idol of the younger part of the company, who laughed at everything he said or did, and at every turn of his countenance. I could not wonder at it, for he must have been a miracle of accomplishments in their eyes. He could imitate Punch and Judy; make an old woman of his hand, with the assistance of a burnt cork and pocket-handkerchief; and cut an orange into such a ludicrous caricature that the young folks were ready to die with laughing.

I was let briefly into his history by Frank Bracebridge. He was an old bachelor, of a small, independent income, which, by careful management, was sufficient for all his wants. He revolved through the family system like a vagrant comet in its orbit; sometimes visiting one branch, and sometimes another quite remote, as is often the case with gentlemen of extensive

oblong form, thereby representing the manger in which, on that occasion, these sages found the infant Jesus.

connections and small fortunes in England. He had a chirping, buoyant disposition, always enjoying the present moment; and his frequent change of scene and company prevented his acquiring those rusty, unaccommodating habits, with which old bachelors are so uncharitably charged. He was a complete family chronicle, being versed in the genealogy, history, and intermarriages of the whole house of Bracebridge, which made him a great favorite with the old folks; he was a beau of all the elder ladies and superannuated spinsters, among whom he was habitually considered rather a young fellow, and he was master of the revels among the children; so that there was not a more popular being in the sphere in which he moved than Mr. Simon Bracebridge. Of late years he had resided almost entirely with the Squire, to whom he had become a factotum, and whom he particularly delighted by jumping with his humor in respect to old times, and by having a scrap of an old song to suit every occasion. We had presently a specimen of his last-mentioned talent, for no sooner was supper removed, and spiced wines and other beverages peculiar to the season introduced, than Master Simon was called on for a good old Christmas song. He bethought himself for a moment, and then, with a sparkle of the eye, and a voice that was by no means bad, excepting that it ran occasionally into a falsetto, like the notes of a split reed, he quavered forth a quaint old ditty: —

> " Now Christmas is come,
> Let us beat up the drum,
> And call all our neighbors together;
> And when they appear,
> Let us make such a cheer
> As will keep out the wind and the weather," etc.

The supper had disposed every one to gayety, and an old harper was summoned from the servants' hall, where he had been strumming all the evening, and to all appearance comforting himself with some of the Squire's home-brewed. He was a kind of hanger-on, I was told, of the establishment. and, though ostensibly a resident of the village, was oftener to be found in the Squire's kitchen than his own home, the old gentleman being fond of the sound of "harp in hall."

The dance, like most dances after supper, was a merry one. Some of the older folks joined in it, and the Squire himself figured down several couple with a partner with whom he affirmed he had danced at every Christmas for nearly half a century. Master Simon, who seemed to be a kind of connecting link between the old times and the new, and to be withal a little antiquated in the taste of his accomplishments, evidently piqued himself on his dancing, and was endeavoring to gain credit by the heel and toe, rigadoon, and other graces of the ancient school; but he had unluckily assorted himself with a little romping girl from boarding-school, who, by her wild vivacity, kept him continually on the stretch, and defeated all his sober attempts at elegance — such are the ill-assorted matches to which antique gentlemen are unfortunately prone!

The young Oxonian, on the contrary, had led out one of his maiden aunts, on whom the rogue played a thousand little knaveries with impunity. He was full of practical jokes, and his delight was to tease his aunts and cousins; yet, like all madcap youngsters, he was a universal favorite among the women. The most interesting couple in the dance was the young officer and a ward of the Squire's, a beautiful, blushing girl of seventeen. From several shy glances which I had noticed in the course of the evening, I suspected there was a little kindness growing up between them; and, indeed, the young soldier was just the hero to captivate a romantic girl. He was tall, slender, and handsome, and, like most young British officers of late years, had picked up various small accomplishments on the Continent, — he could talk French and Italian, draw landscapes, sing very tolerably, dance divinely, — but, above all, he had been wounded at Waterloo.[1] What girl of seventeen, well read in

[1] The French under Napoleon were defeated by the English, June 18, 1815, at Waterloo, a village in Belgium.

poetry and romance, could resist such a mirror of chivalry and perfection!

The moment the dance was over, he caught up a guitar, and, lolling against the old marble fireplace, in an attitude which I am half inclined to suspect was studied, began the little French air of the "Troubadour." The Squire, however, exclaimed against having anything on Christmas Eve but good old English; upon which the young minstrel, casting up his eye for a moment, as if in an effort of memory, struck into another strain, and, with a charming air of gallantry, gave Herrick's[1] "Night-Piece to Julia:"—

> "Her eyes the glow-worm lend thee.
> The shooting stars attend thee,
>   And the elves also,
>   Whose little eyes glow
> Like the sparks of fire, befriend thee.

> "No Will-o'-the-Wisp mislight thee;
> Nor snake or slow-worm bite thee;
>   But on, on thy way,
>   Not making a stay,
> Since ghost there is none to affright thee.

> "Then let not the dark thee cumber;
> What though the moon does slumber,
>   The stars of the night
>   Will lend thee their light,
> Like tapers clear without number.

> "Then, Julia, let me woo thee,
> Thus, thus to come unto me;
>   And when I shall meet
>   Thy silvery feet,
> My soul I'll pour into thee."

The song might or might not have been intended in compliment to the fair Julia, for so I found his partner was called. She, however, was certainly unconscious of any such application,

---

[1] An English poet and clergyman (1591-1674). As a writer of pastoral lyrics, Herrick takes a high rank in English literature.

for she never looked at the singer, but kept her eyes cast upon the floor. Her face was suffused, it is true, with a beautiful blush, and there was a gentle heaving of the bosom; but all that was doubtless caused by the exercise of the dance. Indeed, so great was her indifference, that she was amusing herself with plucking to pieces a choice bouquet of hothouse flowers, and by the time the song was concluded the nosegay lay in ruins on the floor.

The party now broke up for the night with the kind-hearted old custom of shaking hands. As I passed through the hall, on my way to my chamber, the dying embers of the Yule clog still sent forth a dusky glow; and, had it not been the season when "no spirit dare stir abroad," [1] I should have been half tempted to steal from my room at midnight, and peep whether the fairies might not be at their revels about the hearth.

My chamber was in the old part of the mansion, the ponderous furniture of which might have been fabricated in the days of the giants. The room was paneled with cornices of heavy carved work, in which flowers and grotesque faces were strangely intermingled; and a row of black-looking portraits stared mournfully at me from the walls. The bed was of rich though faded damask, with a lofty tester,[2] and stood in a niche opposite a bow-window. I had scarcely got into bed, when a strain of music seemed to break forth in the air just below the window. I listened, and found it proceeded from a band, which I concluded to be the waits [3] from some neighboring village. They went round the house, playing under the windows. I drew aside the curtains to hear them more distinctly. The moonbeams fell through the upper part of the casement, partially lighting up the antiquated apartment. The sounds, as they receded, became more soft and

---

[1] It is an old superstition, that on the eve of Christmas "the bird of dawning singeth all night long" to scare away all evil things from infesting the hallowed hours.

[2] Old French, *testiere* ("a headpiece"); Latin, *testa* ("a shell"). The material stretched over a four-posted bed, forming a canopy over it.

[3] See Note 2, p. 28.

aerial, and seemed to accord with quiet and moonlight. I listened and listened. They became more and more tender and remote; and, as they gradually died away, my head sunk upon the pillow, and I fell asleep.

CHRISTMAS DAY.

> *" Dark and dull night flie hence away,*
> *And give the honor to this day*
> *That sees December turn'd to May.*
>
> *. . . . . . .*
>
> *Why does the chilling winter's morne*
> *Smile like a field beset with corn?*
> *Or smell like to a meade new-shorne,*
> *Thus on the sudden?—come and see*
> *The cause, why things thus fragrant be."*
>
> HERRICK.

WHEN I woke the next morning, it seemed as if all the events of the preceding evening had been a dream, and nothing but the identity of the ancient chamber convinced me of their reality. While I lay musing on my pillow, I heard the sound of little feet pattering outside of the door, and a whispering consultation. Presently a choir of small voices chanted forth an old Christmas carol, the burden of which was,—

> *" Rejoice, our Saviour he was born*
> *On Christmas Day in the morning."*

I rose softly, slipped on my clothes, opened the door suddenly, and beheld one of the most beautiful little fairy groups that a painter could imagine. It consisted of a boy and two girls, the eldest not more than six, and lovely as seraphs. They were going the rounds of the house, singing at every chamber door; but my sudden appearance frightened them into mute bashfulness. They remained for a moment playing on their lips with their fingers, and now and then stealing a shy glance from under their eyebrows; until, as if by one impulse, they scampered away, and, as they turned an angle of the gallery, I heard them laughing in triumph at their escape.

Everything conspired to produce kind and happy feelings in this stronghold of old-fashioned hospitality. The window of my chamber looked out upon what in summer would have been a beautiful landscape. There was a sloping lawn, a fine stream winding at the foot of it, and a tract of park beyond, with noble clumps of trees, and herds of deer. At a distance was a neat hamlet, with the smoke from the cottage chimneys hanging over it, and a church with its dark spire in strong relief against the clear, cold sky. The house was surrounded with evergreens, according to the English custom, which would have given almost an appearance of summer; but the morning was extremely frosty. The light vapor of the preceding evening had been precipitated by the cold, and covered all the trees and every blade of grass with its fine crystallizations. The rays of a bright morning sun had a dazzling effect among the glittering foliage. A robin, perched upon the top of a mountain ash that hung its clusters of red berries just before my window, was basking himself in the sunshine, and piping a few querulous notes; and a peacock was displaying all the glories of his train, and strutting with the pride and gravity of a Spanish grandee [1] on the terrace walk below.

I had scarcely dressed myself, when a servant appeared to invite me to family prayers. He showed me the way to a small chapel in the old wing of the house, where I found the principal part of the family already assembled in a kind of gallery, furnished with cushions, hassocks, and large prayer-books: the servants were seated on benches below. The old gentleman read prayers from a desk in front of the gallery, and Master Simon acted as clerk, and made the responses; and I must do him the justice to say that he acquitted himself with great gravity and decorum.

The service was followed by a Christmas carol, which Mr.

---

[1] A Spanish nobleman, especially one of the first rank (Spanish, *grande*).

Bracebridge himself had constructed from a poem of his favorite author, Herrick; and it had been adapted to a church melody by Master Simon. As there were several good voices among the household, the effect was extremely pleasing; but I was particularly gratified by the exaltation of heart, and sudden sally of grateful feeling, with which the worthy Squire delivered one stanza; his eye glistening, and his voice rambling out of all the bounds of time and tune,—

> " 'Tis thou that crown'st my glittering hearth
> With guiltless mirth,
> And giv'st me Wassaile bowles to drink
> Spic'd to the brink:
> Lord, 'tis thy plenty-dropping hand
> That soiles my land: [1]
> And giv'st me for my bushell sowne,
> Twice ten for one."

I afterwards understood that early morning service was read on every Sunday and saint's day throughout the year, either by Mr. Bracebridge or some member of the family. It was once almost universally the case at the seats of the nobility and gentry of England, and it is much to be regretted that the custom is falling into neglect; for the dullest observer must be sensible of the order and serenity prevalent in those households where the occasional exercise of a beautiful form of worship in the morning gives, as it were, the keynote to every temper for the day, and attunes every spirit to harmony.

Our breakfast consisted of what the Squire denominated true old English fare. He indulged in some bitter lamentations over modern breakfasts of tea and toast, which he censured as among the causes of modern effeminacy and weak nerves, and the decline of old English heartiness; and, though he admitted them to his table to suit the palates of his guests, yet there was a brave display of cold meats, wine, and ale on the sideboard.

After breakfast I walked about the grounds with Frank Brace-

---

[1] Enriches the soil, and sends a plentiful harvest.

bridge and Master Simon, or Mr. Simon, as he was called by everybody but the Squire. We were escorted by a number of gentlemanlike dogs, that seemed loungers about the establishment, from the frisking spaniel to the steady old stag-hound, the last of which was of a race that had been in the family time out of mind. They were all obedient to a dog-whistle which hung to Master Simon's buttonhole, and in the midst of their gambols would glance an eye occasionally upon a small switch he carried in his hand.

The old mansion had a still more venerable look in the yellow sunshine than by pale moonlight; and I could not but feel the force of the Squire's idea, that the formal terraces, heavily molded balustrades, and clipped yew-trees, carried with them an air of proud aristocracy.

There appeared to be an unusual number of peacocks about the place; and I was making some remarks upon what I termed a flock of them, that were basking under a sunny wall, when I was gently corrected in my phraseology by Master Simon, who told me, that, according to the most ancient and approved treatise on hunting, I must say a *muster* of peacocks. " In the same way," added he, with a slight air of pedantry, " we say a flight of doves or swallows; a bevy of quails; a herd of deer, of wrens, or cranes; a skulk of foxes; or a building of rooks." He went on to inform me, that, according to Sir Anthony Fitzherbert,[1] we ought to ascribe to this bird " both understanding and glory; for, being praised, he will presently set up his tail, chiefly against the sun, to the intent you may the better behold the beauty thereof. But at the fall of the leaf, when his tail falleth, he will mourn and hide himself in corners, till his tail come again as it was." [2]

[1] An eminent English lawyer, who wrote, in 1523, The Book of Husbandry, — the first published work on agriculture in the English language.

[2] The peacock is said to be the vainest of birds. It came originally from India. It was there that Alexander the Great saw it for the first time. He was so impressed with its magnificent plumage, that he forbade all persons, under pain of death, to kill any.

I could not help smiling at this display of small erudition on so whimsical a subject : but I found that the peacocks were birds of some consequence at the hall ; for Frank Bracebridge informed me that they were great favorites with his father, who was extremely careful to keep up the breed, partly because they belonged to chivalry, and were in great request at the stately banquets of the olden time,[1] and partly because they had a pomp and magnificence about them highly becoming an old family mansion. Nothing, he was accustomed to say, had an air of greater state and dignity than a peacock perched upon an antique stone balustrade.

Master Simon had now to hurry off, having an appointment at the parish church with the village choristers, who were to perform some music of his selection. There was something extremely agreeable in the cheerful flow of animal spirits of the little man ; and I confess I had been somewhat surprised at his apt quotations from authors who certainly were not in the range of everyday reading. I mentioned this last circumstance to Frank Bracebridge, who told me with a smile that Master Simon's whole stock of erudition was confined to some half a dozen old authors, which the Squire had put into his hands, and which he read over and over whenever he had a studious fit, as he sometimes had on a rainy day or a long winter evening. Sir Anthony Fitzherbert's "Book of Husbandry ;" Markham's "Country Contentments ;"[2] the "Tretyse of Hunting," by Sir Thomas Cockayne,[3] Knight; Izaak Walton's [4] "Angler ;" and two or three more such ancient

[1] Quintus Hortensius, the orator, was the first to have peacocks served at a banquet. After this no banquet was complete without this dish.

[2] See Note 2, p. 55.

[3] Cokaine or Cokayn (written also Cockaine), an English Catholic (born in Derbyshire, 1608 ; died, 1684). was a Royalist in the civil war. He composed some worthless plays and doggerel poems, which are only worthy of notice on account of the anecdotes they furnish of contemporary authors or actors.

[4] A celebrated English writer (born at Stafford, 1593 ; died, 1683). His principal work, The Complete Angler or Contemplative Man's Recreation, was published in 1653.

worthies of the pen, — were his standard authorities; and, like all men who know but a few books, he looked up to them with a kind of idolatry, and quoted them on all occasions. As to his songs, they were chiefly picked out of old books in the Squire's library, and adapted to tunes that were popular among the choice spirits of the last century. His practical application of scraps of literature, however, had caused him to be looked upon as a prodigy of book knowledge by all the grooms, huntsmen, and small sportsmen of the neighborhood.

While we were talking, we heard the distant toll of the village bell, and I was told that the Squire was a little particular in having his household at church on a Christmas morning, considering it a day of pouring out of thanks and rejoicing; for, as old Tusser [1] observed, —

> " At Christmas be merry, *and thankful withal,*
> And feast thy poor neighbors, the great with the small."

"If you are disposed to go to church," said Frank Bracebridge, "I can promise you a specimen of my cousin Simon's musical achievements. As the church is destitute of an organ, he has formed a band from the village amateurs, and established a musical club for their improvement; he has also sorted a choir, as he sorted my father's pack of hounds, according to the directions of Jervaise Markham [2] in his ' Country Contentments.' For the bass he has sought out all the ' deep, solemn mouths,' and for the tenor the 'loud-ringing mouth,' among the country bumpkins; and for 'sweet mouths,' he has culled with curious taste among the prettiest lasses in the neighborhood, though these last, he affirms, are the most difficult to keep in tune, your pretty fe-

[1] Thomas Tusser (1527-80), poet, was born at Essex, England. His poems on husbandry have the charm of simplicity and directness, and during his life they went through a number of editions.

[2] Jervaise (or Gervase) Markham, an English soldier and miscellaneous writer, was born in Nottinghamshire about 1570. He served in the Royalist in the civil war, and died in 1655.

male singer being exceedingly wayward and capricious, and very liable to accident."

As the morning, though frosty, was remarkably fine and clear, the most of the family walked to the church, which was a very old building of gray stone, and stood near a village, about half a mile from the park gate. Adjoining it was a low, snug parsonage, which seemed coeval with the church. The front of it was perfectly matted with a yew-tree that had been trained against its walls, through the dense foliage of which apertures had been formed to admit light into the small antique lattices. As we passed this sheltered nest, the parson issued forth, and preceded us.

I had expected to see a sleek, well-conditioned pastor, such as is often found in a snug living in the vicinity of a rich patron's table, but I was disappointed. The parson was a little, meager, black-looking man, with a grizzled wig that was too wide, and stood off from each ear, so that his head seemed to have shrunk away within it, like a dried filbert in its shell. He wore a rusty coat, with great skirts, and pockets that would have held the church Bible and Prayer Book; and his small legs seemed still smaller, from being planted in large shoes decorated with enormous buckles.

I was informed by Frank Bracebridge that the parson had been a chum of his father's at Oxford,[1] and had received this living shortly after the latter had come to his estate. He was a complete black-letter[2] hunter, and would scarcely read a work printed in the Roman character. The editions of Caxton and Wynkin de Worde were his delight; and he was indefatigable in his researches after such Old English writers as have fallen into oblivion from their worthlessness. In deference, perhaps, to the notions of Mr. Bracebridge, he had made diligent investigations

[1] The famous university situated in Oxford, the county town of Oxfordshire.

[2] A type which appeared in England about the year 1480. It was used especially for Bibles, law-books, royal proclamations, etc.

into the festive rites and holiday customs of former times, and had been as zealous in the inquiry as if he had been a boon companion; but it was merely with that plodding spirit with which men of adust temperament follow up any track of study, merely because it is denominated learning; indifferent to its intrinsic nature, whether it be the illustration of the wisdom or of the ribaldry and obscenity of antiquity. He had pored over these old volumes so intensely, that they seemed to have been reflected into his countenance; which, if the face be indeed an index of the mind, might be compared to a title-page of black-letter.

On reaching the church porch, we found the parson rebuking the gray-headed sexton for having used mistletoe among the greens with which the church was decorated. It was, he observed, an unholy plant, profaned by having been used by the Druids in their mystic ceremonies; and though it might be innocently employed in the festive ornamenting of halls and kitchens, yet it had been deemed by the fathers of the Church as unhallowed, and totally unfit for sacred purposes. So tenacious was he on this point, that the poor sexton was obliged to strip down a great part of the humble trophies of his taste, before the parson would consent to enter upon the service of the day.

The interior of the church was venerable but simple. On the walls were several mural monuments of the Bracebridges; and just beside the altar was a tomb of ancient workmanship, on which lay the effigy of a warrior in armor, with his legs crossed, — a sign of his having been a crusader. I was told it was one of the family who had signalized himself in the Holy Land, and the same whose picture hung over the fireplace in the hall.

During service, Master Simon stood up in the pew, and repeated the responses very audibly, evincing that kind of ceremonious devotion punctually observed by a gentleman of the old school, and a man of old family connections. I observed, too, that he turned over the leaves of a folio Prayer Book with something of a flourish; possibly to show off an enormous seal-ring which enriched one of his fingers, and which had the look of a family relic. But he was evidently most solicitous about the musical part of the service, keeping his eye fixed intently on the choir, and beating time with much gesticulation and emphasis.

The orchestra was in a small gallery, and presented a most whimsical grouping of heads, piled one above the other, among which I particularly noticed that of the village tailor, a pale fellow with a retreating forehead and chin, who played on the clarinet, and seemed to have blown his face to a point; and there was another, a short, pursy man, stooping and laboring at a bass viol, so as to show nothing but the top of a round, bald head, like the egg of an ostrich. There were two or three pretty faces among the female singers, to which the keen air of a frosty morning had given a bright, rosy tint; but the gentlemen choristers had evidently been chosen, like old Cremona [1] fiddles, more for tone than looks; and, as several had to sing from the same book, there were clusterings of odd physiognomies, not unlike those groups of cherubs we sometimes see on country tombstones.

The usual services of the choir were managed tolerably well, the vocal parts generally lagging a little behind the instrumental, and some loitering fiddler now and then making up for lost time by traveling over a passage with prodigious celerity, and clearing more bars than the keenest fox-hunter to be in at the death. But the great trial was an anthem that had been prepared and arranged by Master Simon, and on which he had founded great expectation. Unluckily, there was a blunder at the very outset. The musicians became flurried; Master Simon was in a fever; everything went on lamely and irregularly until they came to a chorus beginning, "Now let us sing with one accord," which seemed to be a signal for parting company. All became discord and confusion. Each shifted for himself, and got to the end as

---

[1] The capital of a province of Lombardy, also named Cremona, formerly celebrated for its violins and other musical instruments. Great prices were paid for violins made in Cremona The manufacture of these has now declined.

well, or rather as soon, as he could, excepting one old chorister in a pair of horn spectacles, bestriding and pinching a long, sonorous nose, who, happening to stand a little apart, and being wrapped up in his own melody, kept on a quivering course, wriggling his head, ogling his book, and winding all up by a nasal solo of at least three bars' duration.

The parson gave us a most erudite sermon on the rites and ceremonies of Christmas, and the propriety of observing it not merely as a day of thanksgiving, but of rejoicing; supporting the correctness of his opinions by the earliest usages of the Church, and enforcing them by the authorities of Theophilus of Cæsarea,[1] St. Cyprian,[2] St. Chrysostom,[3] St. Augustine,[4] and a cloud more of saints and fathers, from whom he made copious quotations. I was a little at a loss to perceive the necessity of such a mighty array of forces to maintain a point which no one present seemed inclined to dispute, but I soon found that the good man had a legion of ideal adversaries to contend with, having, in the course of his researches on the subject of Christmas, got completely embroiled in the sectarian controversies of the Revolution, when the Puritans made such a fierce assault upon the ceremonies of the Church, and poor old Christmas was driven out of the land by proclamation of Parliament.[5] The worthy parson lived but with times past, and knew but little of the present.

[1] Instructor of Justinian, and abbot of St. Alexander at Prisrend in Macedonia, afterwards Bishop of Sardica in 517.

[2] Bishop of Carthage in the third century, one of the most illustrious men in the early history of the Church, and one of the most notable of its early martyrs. He was ordered to be beheaded Sept. 14, 258, by Emperor Valerian.

[3] The most famous of the Greek fathers (born at Antioch about 347). The festival of St. Chrysostom is observed both in the Greek and in the Latin Church, — by the former on Nov. 13, and by the latter on Jan. 27.

[4] The greatest of the four great fathers of the Latin Church (born in Numidia, Nov. 13, A.D. 354).

[5] "The House spent much time this day about the business of the Navy, for settling the affairs at sea, and before they rose, were presented with a ter-

Shut up among worm-eaten tomes in the retirement of his antiquated little study, the pages of old times were to him as the
gazettes of the day, while the era of the Revolution was mere
modern history.   He forgot that nearly two centuries had elapsed
since the fiery persecution of poor mince pie throughout the land,
when plum porridge was denounced as "mere popery," and roast-
beef as anti-Christian, and that Christmas had been brought in
again triumphantly with the merry court of King Charles at the
Restoration.   He kindled into warmth with the ardor of his contest, and the host of imaginary foes with whom he had to combat.   He had a stubborn conflict with old Prynne[1] and two or
three other forgotten champions of the Roundheads,[2] on the subject of Christmas festivity, and concluded by urging his hearers,
in the most solemn and affecting manner, to stand to the traditional customs of their fathers, and feast and make merry on this
joyful anniversary of the Church.

I have seldom known a sermon attended apparently with more
immediate effects; for, on leaving the church, the congregation
seemed, one and all, possessed with the gayety of spirit so ear-

rible remonstrance against Christmas day, grounded upon divine Scriptures,
2 Cor. v. 16, 1 Cor. xv. 14, 17; and in honor of the Lord's Day, grounded
upon these Scriptures, John xx. 1, Rev. i. 10, Psalms cxviii. 24, Lev. xxiii.
7, 11, Mark xv. 8, Psalms lxxxiv. 10; in which Christmas is called Anti-
christ's masse, and those Masse-mongers and Papists who observe it, etc.
In consequence of which Parliament spent some time in consultation about
the abolition of Christmas day, passed orders to that effect, and resolved to
sit on the following day, which was commonly called Christmas day."—
Flying Eagle (a small gazette published Dec. 24, 1652).

[1] William Prynne (1600–69) was a Puritan to the core.   He published in
1633 a book (Histrio-Mastix) which was an attack upon stage plays.   The
Queen was very much interested in the drama at this time, and Prynne's
offensive words were supposed to apply to her.   Prynne was sentenced by the
Star Chamber to fine, imprisonment, and to be set in the pillory, where he
was to lose both his ears.

[2] Adherents of the Parliamentary or Puritan party, as opposed to the
Royalists; called Roundheads in derisive allusion to their close-cut hair, the
Royalists usually wearing theirs long.

nestly enjoined by their pastor. The elder folks gathered in knots in the churchyard, greeting and shaking hands; and the children ran about crying, "Ule! Ule!" and repeating some uncouth rhymes,[1] which the parson, who had joined us, informed me had been handed down from days of yore. The villagers doffed their hats to the Squire as he passed, giving him the good wishes of the season with every appearance of heartfelt sincerity, and were invited by him to the hall, to take something to keep out the cold of the weather; and I heard blessings uttered by several of the poor, which convinced me, that, in the midst of his enjoyments, the worthy old cavalier had not forgotten the true Christmas virtue of charity.

On our way homeward his heart seemed overflowing with generous and happy feelings. As we passed over a rising ground which commanded something of a prospect, the sounds of rustic merriment now and then reached our ears. The Squire paused for a few moments, and looked around with an air of inexpressible benignity. The beauty of the day was of itself sufficient to inspire philanthropy. Notwithstanding the frostiness of the morning, the sun, in his cloudless journey, had acquired sufficient power to melt away the thin covering of snow from every southern declivity, and to bring out the living green which adorns an English landscape even in mid-winter. Large tracts of smiling verdure contrasted with the dazzling whiteness of the shaded slopes and hollows. Every sheltered bank on which the broad rays rested yielded its silver rill of cold and limpid water, glittering through the dripping grass, and sent up slight exhalations to contribute to the thin haze that hung just above the surface of the earth. There was something truly cheering in this triumph of warmth and verdure over the frosty thraldom of winter: it was, as the Squire observed, an emblem of Christmas hospital-

[1] IRVING'S NOTE: —

> "Ule! Ule!
> Three puddings in a pule;
> Crack nuts and cry ule!"

ity, breaking through the chills of ceremony and selfishness, and
thawing every heart into a flow. He pointed with pleasure to
the indications of good cheer reeking from the chimneys of the
comfortable farmhouses and low thatched cottages. "I love,"
said he, "to see this day well kept by rich and poor. It is a
great thing to have one day in the year, at least, when you are
sure of being welcome wherever you go, and of having, as it
were, the world all thrown open to you; and I am almost disposed to join with Poor Robin, in his malediction on every churl-
ish enemy to this honest festival: —

> " ' Those who at Christmas do repine,
>   And would fain hence dispatch him,
>   May they with old Duke Humphry dine,
>   Or else may Squire Ketch[1] catch 'em.' "

The Squire went on to lament the deplorable decay of the
games and amusements which were once prevalent at this season
among the lower orders, and countenanced by the higher, when
the old halls of castles and manor-houses were thrown open
at daylight, when the tables were covered with brawn and beef
and humming ale, when the harp and the carol resounded all day
long, and when rich and poor were alike welcome to enter and
make merry.[2] "Our old games and local customs," said he,
"had a great effect in making the peasant fond of his home, and
the promotion of them by the gentry made him fond of his lord.

[1] Alluding to Jack Ketch, the hangman (1678). Ketch executed Lord
Russell and the Duke of Monmouth. The name has become proverbial for
hangmen.

[2] "An English gentleman at the opening of the great day, i.e. on Christmas day in the morning, had all his tenants and neighbors enter his hall by
daybreak. The strong beer was broached, and the black jacks went plenti-
fully about with toast, sugar, and nutmeg, and good Cheshire cheese. The
Hackin (the great sausage) must be boiled by daybreak, or else two young
men must take the maiden (i.e. the cook) by the arms and run her round
the market place till she is shamed of her laziness." — *Round about our Sea-
Coal Fire.*

They made the times merrier and kinder and better, and I can truly say, with one of our old poets,—

> " ' I like them well — the curious preciseness
>   And all-pretended gravity of those
>   That seek to banish hence these harmless sports,
>   Have thrust away much ancient honesty.'

"The nation," continued he, "is altered. We have almost lost our simple, true-hearted peasantry. They have broken asunder from the higher classes, and seem to think their interests are separate. They have become too knowing, and begin to read newspapers, listen to ale-house politicians, and talk of reform. I think one mode to keep them in good humor in these hard times would be for the nobility and gentry to pass more time on their estates, mingle more among the country people, and set the merry old English games going again."

Such was the good Squire's project for mitigating public discontent; and, indeed, he had once attempted to put his doctrine in practice, and a few years before had kept open house during the holidays in the old style. The country people, however, did not understand how to play their parts in the scene of hospitality. Many uncouth circumstances occurred. The manor was overrun by all the vagrants of the country, and more beggars drawn into the neighborhood in one week than the parish officers could get rid of in a year. Since then he had contented himself with inviting the decent part of the neighboring peasantry to call at the hall on Christmas Day, and with distributing beef and bread and ale among the poor, that they might make merry in their own dwellings.

We had not been long home, when the sound of music was heard from a distance. A band of country lads, without coats, their shirt-sleeves fancifully tied with ribbons, their hats decorated with greens, and clubs in their hands, were seen advancing up the avenue, followed by a large number of villagers and peasantry. They stopped before the hall door, where the music struck up a peculiar air, and the lads performed a curious and intricate dance, advancing, retreating, and striking their clubs together, keeping exact time to the music; while one, whimsically crowned with a fox's skin, the tail of which flaunted down his back, kept capering round the skirts of the dance, and rattling a Christmas box [1] with many antic gesticulations.

The Squire eyed this fanciful exhibition with great interest and delight, and gave me a full account of its origin, which he traced to the times when the Romans held possession of the island; plainly proving that this was a lineal descendant of the sword dance of the ancients. It was now, he said, nearly extinct, but he had accidentally met with traces of it in the neighborhood, and had encouraged its revival; though, to tell the truth, it was too apt to be followed up by rough cudgel play,[2] and broken heads in the evening.

After the dance was concluded, the whole party was entertained with brawn and beef, and stout home-brewed. The Squire himself mingled among the rustics, and was received with awkward demonstrations of deference and regard. It is true, I perceived two or three of the younger peasants, as they were raising their tankards to their mouths, when the Squire's back was turned, making something of a grimace, and giving each other the wink; but, the moment they caught my eye, they pulled grave faces,

---

[1] This title has been said to have been derived from the box which was kept on board of every vessel that sailed upon a distant voyage, for the reception of donations to the priest, who, in return, was expected to offer masses for the safety of the expedition, to the particular saint having charge of the ship, and, above all, of the box. The mass was at that time called "Christ mass," and the boxes kept to pay for it were of course called "Christ-mass boxes." The poor were in the habit of begging from the rich to contribute to the mass boxes, and hence the title which has descended to our day. A relic of these ancient boxes yet exists, in the earthen or wooden box, with a slit in it, which still bears the same name, and is carried by servants and children for the purpose of gathering money at Christmas, being broken only when the period of collection is supposed to be over.

[2] A bout with cudgels. Cudgels were thick short sticks, or staves.

and were exceedingly demure. With Master Simon, however, they all seemed more at their ease. His varied occupations and amusements had made him well known throughout the neighborhood. He was a visitor at every farmhouse and cottage; gossiped with the farmers and their wives; romped with their daughters; and, like that type of a vagrant bachelor the humble-bee, tolled the sweets from all the rosy lips of the country round.

The bashfulness of the guests soon gave way before good cheer and affability. There is something genuine and affectionate in the gayety of the lower orders, when it is excited by the bounty and familiarity of those above them. The warm glow of gratitude enters into their mirth; and a kind word or a small pleasantry, frankly uttered by a patron, gladdens the heart of the dependant more than oil and wine. When the Squire had retired, the merriment increased; and there was much joking and laughter, particularly between Master Simon and a hale, ruddy-faced, white-headed farmer, who appeared to be the wit of the village, for I observed all his companions to wait with open mouths for his retorts, and burst into a gratuitous laugh before they could well understand them.

The whole house, indeed, seemed abandoned to merriment. As I passed to my room to dress for dinner, I heard the sound of music in a small court, and, looking through a window that commanded it, I perceived a band of wandering musicians, with pandean[1] pipes and tambourine. A pretty, coquettish house-maid was dancing a jig with a smart country lad, while several of the other servants were looking on. In the midst of her sport, the girl caught a glimpse of my face at the window, and, coloring up, ran off with an air of roguish affected confusion.

---

[1] Pan, in Greek mythology, was the god of forests, pastures, and flocks, and was the attributed inventor of the shepherd's flute or pipe, the syrinx, — a series of graduated tubes set together (open at one end, and closed at the other), played by blowing across the open ends.

THE CHRISTMAS DINNER.

> *" Lo, now is come our joyful'st feast!*
> *Let every man be jolly,*
> *Each roome with yvie leaves is drest,*
> *And every post with holly.*
> *Now all our neighbours' chimneys smoke,*
> *And Christmas blocks are burning;*
> *Their ovens they with bak't meats choke,*
> *And all their spits are turning.*
> *Without the door let sorrow lie,*
> *And if, for cold, it hap to die,*
> *Wee'l bury 't in a Christmas pye,*
> *And evermore be merry."* *
>
> WITHERS,[1] *Juvenilia.*

I HAD finished my toilet, and was loitering with Frank Brace-bridge in the library, when we heard a distant thwacking sound, which he informed me was a signal for the serving-up of the dinner. The Squire kept up old customs in kitchen as well as hall; and the rolling-pin, struck upon the dresser by the cook, summoned the servants to carry in the meats.

> " Just in this nick the cook knock'd thrice,
> And all the waiters in a trice,
> His summons did obey;
> Each serving man, with dish in hand,
> Marched boldly up, like our train band,
> Presented, and away."[2]

The dinner was served up in the great hall, where the Squire always held his Christmas banquet. A blazing, crackling fire of logs had been heaped on to warm the spacious apartment, and the flame went sparkling and wreathing up the wide-mouthed chimney. The great picture of the crusader and his white horse had been profusely decorated with greens for the occasion; and

---

[1] Written also Wither and Wyther. An English poet, satirist, and political writer (1588–1667).

[2] From Sir John Suckling, an English poet (born in Middlesex about 1608, died about 1642), celebrated as a wit at the court of Charles I.

holly and ivy had likewise been wreathed round the helmet and weapons on the opposite wall, which I understood were the arms of the same warrior. I must own, by the by, I had strong doubts about the authenticity of the painting and armor as having belonged to the crusader, they certainly having the stamp of more recent days; but I was told that the painting had been so considered time out of mind, and that, as to the armor, it had been found in a lumber-room, and elevated to its present situation by the Squire, who at once determined it to be the armor of the family hero; and, as he was absolute authority on all such subjects in his own household, the matter had passed into current acceptation. A sideboard was set out just under this chivalric trophy, on which was a display of plate that might have vied (at least in variety) with Belshazzar's [1] parade of the vessels of the temple, — "flagons, cans, cups, beakers, goblets, basins, and ewers," the gorgeous utensils of good companionship that had gradually accumulated through many generations of jovial housekeepers. Before these stood the two Yule candles,[2] beaming like two stars of the first magnitude; other lights were distributed in branches; and the whole array glittered like a firmament of silver.

We were ushered into this banqueting scene with the sound of minstrelsy; the old harper being seated on a stool beside the fireplace, and twanging his instrument with a vast deal more power than melody. Never did Christmas board display a more goodly and gracious assemblage of countenances. Those who were not handsome were at least happy, and happiness is a rare improver of your hard-favored visage. I always consider an old English family as well worth studying as a collection of Holbein's [3] por-

---

[1] Son of Nabunahid, King of Babylon; conquered by the Persians and Cyrus, 556 B.C. (Compare Daniel v. 2.)

[2] These were large candles lighted and burned at Christmas Eve festivities. It was considered by many bad luck if the candle burned out before the close of the evening; and any portion left was kept to be burned at the corpse watch, or lich wake, of the owner.

[3] Hans Holbein (born at Grünstadt in 1497, died in 1543) was one of the

traits or Albert Dürer's [1] prints.   There is much antiquarian lore
to be acquired, much knowledge of the physiognomies of former
times.   Perhaps it may be from having continually before their
eyes those rows of old family portraits with which the mansions
of this country are stocked: certain it is, that the quaint features
of antiquity are often most faithfully perpetuated in these ancient
lines; and I have traced an old family nose through a whole
picture gallery, legitimately handed down from generation to
generation, almost from the time of the Conquest.   Something
of the kind was to be observed in the worthy company around
me.   Many of their faces had evidently originated in a Gothic
age, and been merely copied by succeeding generations; and
there was one little girl in particular, of staid demeanor, with a
high Roman nose and an antique vinegar aspect, who was a
great favorite of the Squire's, being, as he said, a Bracebridge
all over, and the very counterpart of one of his ancestors who
figured in the court of Henry VIII. [2]

The parson said grace, which was not a short familiar one,
such as is commonly addressed to the Deity in these unceremo-
nious days, but a long, courtly, well-worded one of the ancient
school.   There was now a pause, as if something was expected,
when suddenly the butler entered the hall with some degree of
bustle.   He was attended by a servant on each side with a large
wax-light, and bore a silver dish on which was an enormous pig's

most celebrated German painters.   Henry VIII. gave him abundant employment, and also bestowed upon him a large pension.   Holbein was also a
skillful architect and wood-engraver.   His greatest pictures were, " Dance of
Death," the " Adoration of the Shepherds and the Kings," and the " Last
Supper."

[1] Albrecht Dürer (born at Nuremberg in 1471; died there, April, 1528)
has a name, in the history of art, equal to that of the greatest Italians.   A
very choice collection of his drawings (a large volume), forming part of Lord
Arundel's collection, is in the British Museum.

[2] Henry VIII. (born at Greenwich, England, in 1491; died in 1547)
ascended the English throne in the year 1509.   He was the father of Queen
Elizabeth.

head decorated with rosemary,[1] with a lemon in its mouth, which was placed with great formality at the head of the table. The moment this pageant made its appearance, the harper struck up a flourish; at the conclusion of which the young Oxonian, on receiving a hint from the Squire, gave, with an air of the most comic gravity, an old carol, the first verse of which was as follows:—

> " Caput apri defero,[2]
> Reddens laudes Domino.[3]
> The boar's head in hand bring I,
> With garlands gay and rosemary.
> I pray you all synge merily
> Qui estis in convivio." [4]

Though prepared to witness many of these little eccentricities, from being apprised of the peculiar hobby of mine host, yet, I confess, the parade with which so odd a dish was introduced somewhat perplexed me, until I gathered from the conversation of the Squire and the parson that it was meant to represent the bringing-in of the boar's head,—a dish formerly served up with much ceremony, and the sound of minstrelsy and song, at great tables on Christmas Day. "I like the old custom," said the Squire, "not merely because it is stately and pleasing in itself, but because it was observed at the college at Oxford[5] at which I was educated. When I hear the old song chanted, it brings to mind the time when I was young and gamesome; and the noble old college hall; and my fellow-students loitering about in their black gowns, many of whom, poor lads, are now in their graves."

The parson, however, whose mind was not haunted by such

---

[1] Old English, *rosmarine ;* Latin, *rosmarinus* (*ros*, " dew ; " and *marinus*, " of the sea "). So called because it flourishes best in places near the sea. It is very fragrant, and symbolic of remembrance. Compare Hamlet (act iv. sc. 5): " There's rosemary, that's for remembrance."

[2] " I bring the boar's head."

[3] " Returning praises to the Lord."

[4] " As many as are at the banquet."

[5] The famous university situated in the county of Oxfordshire.

associations, and who was always more taken up with the text than the sentiment, objected to the Oxonian's version of the carol, which he affirmed was different from that sung at college. He went on, with the dry perseverance of a commentator, to give the college reading, accompanied by sundry annotations, addressing himself at first to the company at large; but, finding their attention gradually diverted to other talk and other objects, he lowered his tone as his number of auditors diminished, until he concluded his remarks in an under-voice to a fat-headed old gentleman next him, who was silently engaged in the discussion of a huge plateful of turkey.[1]

The table was literally loaded with good cheer, and presented an epitome of country abundance, in this season of overflowing larders. A distinguished post was allotted to "ancient sirloin,"[2]

---

[1] IRVING'S NOTE. — The old ceremony of serving up the boar's head on Christmas Day is still observed in the hall of Queen's College, Oxford. I was favored by the parson with a copy of the carol as now sung; and as it may be acceptable to such of my readers as are curious in these grave and learned matters, I give it entire: —

> "The boar's head in hand bear I,
>   Bedeck'd with bays and rosemary;
> And I pray you, my masters, be merry,
>   Quot estis in convivio.
>   Caput apri defero,
>   Reddens laudes Domino.
>
> "The boar's head, as I understand,
>   Is the rarest dish in all this land,
> Which thus bedeck'd with a gay garland
>   Let us servire cantico.
>   Caput apri defero,
>   Reddens laudes Domino.
>
> "Our steward hath provided this
>   In honour of the King of Bliss,
> Which on this day to be served is
>   In Reginensi Atrio.
>   Caput apri defero,
>   Reddens laudes Domino."

[2] The word is derived from the French *surlonge*, "a sirloin:" *sur* (Latin *super*), "over." and *longe*, "loin." There is, of course. no etymologica\

as mine host termed it; being, as he added, "the standard of old English hospitality, and a joint of goodly presence, and full of expectation." There were several dishes quaintly decorated, and which had evidently something traditional in their embellishments, but about which, as I did not like to appear over-curious, I asked no questions.

I could not, however, but notice a pie, magnificently decorated with peacocks' feathers, in imitation of the tail of that bird, which overshadowed a considerable tract of the table. This, the Squire confessed with some little hesitation, was a pheasant pie, though a peacock pie was certainly the most authentical; but there had been such a mortality among the peacocks this season, that he could not prevail upon himself to have one killed.[1]

It would be tedious, perhaps, to my wiser readers, who may not have that foolish fondness for odd and obsolete things to which I am a little given, were I to mention the other makeshifts of this worthy old humorist, by which he was endeavoring to follow up, though at humble distance, the quaint customs of antiquity. I was pleased, however, to see the respect shown to his whims by his children and relatives; who, indeed, entered readily

---

basis for Richardson's story that James I, on returning from a hunting excursion, so much enjoyed his dinner consisting of a loin of roast beef, that he laid his sword across it, and dubbed it "Sir Loin."

[1] IRVING'S NOTE. — The peacock was anciently in great demand for stately entertainments. Sometimes it was made into a pie, at one end of which the head appeared above the crust in all its plumage, with the beak richly gilt: at the other end the tail was displayed. Such pies were served up at the solemn banquets of chivalry, when knights-errant pledged themselves to undertake any perilous enterprise, whence came the ancient oath, used by Justice Shallow, "by cock and pie." The peacock was also an important dish for the Christmas feast; and Massinger, in his City Madam, gives some idea of the extravagance with which this, as well as other dishes, was prepared for the gorgeous revels of the olden times : —

"Men may talk of Country Christmasses,
 Their thirty pound butter'd eggs, their pies of carps' tongues:
 Their pheasants drench'd with ambergris; *the carcases of three fat wethers
 bruised for gravy to make sauce for a single peacock!*"

into the full spirit of them, and seemed all well versed in their
parts, having doubtless been present at many a rehearsal. I
was amused, too, at the air of profound gravity with which the
butler and other servants executed the duties assigned them,
however eccentric. They had an old-fashioned look,—having,
for the most part, been brought up in the household, and grown
into keeping with the antiquated mansion, and the humors of its
lord,—and most probably looked upon all his whimsical regula-
tions as the established laws of honorable housekeeping.

When the cloth was removed, the butler brought in a huge
silver vessel of rare and curious workmanship, which he placed
before the Squire. Its appearance was hailed with acclamation,
being the wassail bowl, so renowned in Christmas festivity. The
contents had been prepared by the Squire himself; for it was a
beverage in the skillful mixture of which he particularly prided
himself, alleging that it was too abstruse and complex for the
comprehension of an ordinary servant. It was a potation, indeed, that might well make the heart of a toper leap within him,
being composed of the richest and raciest wines, highly spiced
and sweetened, with roasted apples bobbing about the surface.[1]

The old gentleman's whole countenance beamed with a serene
look of indwelling delight as he stirred this mighty bowl. Having raised it to his lips with a hearty wish of a merry Christmas
to all present, he sent it brimming round the board, for every one
to follow his example, according to the primitive style, pronoun-

---

[1] IRVING'S NOTE. — The wassail bowl was sometimes composed of ale
instead of wine, with nutmeg, sugar, toast, ginger, and roasted crabs. In
this way the nut-brown beverage is still prepared in some old families, and
round the hearth of substantial farmers at Christmas. It is also called
"lamb's wool," and it is celebrated by Herrick in his Twelfth Night:—

> "Next crowne the bowle full
>   With gentle Lamb's Wool,
> Add sugar, nutmeg, and ginger,
>   With store of ale too;
>   And thus ye must doe
> To make the Wassaile a swinger."

cing it "the ancient fountain of good feeling, where all hearts met together."[1]

There was much laughing and rallying as the honest emblem of Christmas joviality circulated, and was kissed rather coyly by the ladies; but when it reached Master Simon, he raised it in both hands, and, with the air of a boon companion, struck up an old wassail chanson:[2]—

> " The brown bowle,
> The merry brown bowle,
> As it goes round about-a,
> Fill
> Still,
> Let the world say what it will,
> And drink your fill all out-a,

> "The deep canne,
> The merry deep canne,
> As thou dost freely quaff-a,
> Sing
> Fling,
> Be as merry as a king,
> And sound a lusty laugh-a,"[3]

Much of the conversation during dinner turned upon family topics, to which I was a stranger. There was, however, a great deal of rallying of Master Simon about some gay widow, with whom he was accused of having a flirtation. This attack was commenced by the ladies; but it was continued throughout the dinner by the fat-headed old gentleman next the parson, with the persevering assiduity of a slowhound,[4] being one of those long-winded jokers, who, though rather dull at starting game, are un-rivaled for their talents in hunting it down. At every pause in the general conversation, he renewed his bantering in pretty

---

[1] " The custom of drinking out of the same cup gave place to each having his cup. When the steward came to the doore with the Wassel, he was to cry three times, *Wassel, Wassel, Wassel,* and then the chappell (chaplain) was to answer with a song."—*Archæologia.*

[2] Song.   [3] From Poor Robin's Almanack.   [4] Bloodhound.

much the same terms, winking hard at me with both eyes whenever he gave Master Simon what he considered a home thrust. The latter, indeed, seemed fond of being teased on the subject, as old bachelors are apt to be; and he took occasion to inform me, in an undertone, that the lady in question was a prodigiously fine woman, and drove her own curricle.

The dinner-time passed away in this flow of innocent hilarity, and, though the old hall may have resounded in its time with many a scene of broader rout and revel, yet I doubt whether it ever witnessed more honest and genuine enjoyment. How easy it is for one benevolent being to diffuse pleasure around him; and how truly is a kind heart a fountain of gladness, making everything in its vicinity to freshen into smiles! The joyous disposition of the worthy Squire was perfectly contagious. He was happy himself, and disposed to make all the world happy; and the little eccentricities of his humor did but season, in a manner, the sweetness of his philanthropy.

After the dinner-table was removed, the hall was given up to the younger members of the family, who, prompted to all kind of noisy mirth by the Oxonian and Master Simon, made its old walls ring with their merriment, as they played at romping games. I delight in witnessing the gambols of children, and particularly at this happy holiday season, and could not help stealing out of the drawing-room on hearing one of their peals of laughter. I found them at the game of blind-man's-buff. Master Simon, who was the leader of their revels, and seemed on all occasions to fulfill the office of that ancient potentate, the Lord of Misrule,[1] was blinded in the midst of the hall. The little beings were as busy about him as the mock fairies about Falstaff,[2] pinching

---

1 " At Christmasse there was in the Kinges house, wheresoever hee was lodged, a lorde of misrule, or mayster of merie disportes, and the like had ye in the house of every nobleman of honor, or good worshippe, were he spirituall or temporall." — *Stow.*

2 Sir John Falstaff, one of Shakespeare's characters in The Merry Wives of Windsor and in the two parts of Henry IV.

him, plucking at the skirts of his coat, and tickling him with straws. One fine blue-eyed girl of about thirteen, with her flaxen hair all in beautiful confusion, her frolic face in a glow, her frock half torn off her shoulders, a complete picture of a romp, was the chief tormentor; and from the slyness with which Master Simon avoided the smaller game, and hemmed this wild little nymph in corners, and obliged her to jump, shrieking, over chairs, I suspected the rogue of being not a whit more blinded than was convenient.

When I returned to the drawing-room, I found the company seated round the fire, listening to the parson, who was deeply ensconced in a high-backed, oaken chair, the work of some cunning artificer of yore, which had been brought from the library for his particular accommodation. From this venerable piece of furniture, with which his shadowy figure and dark, weazen face so admirably accorded, he was dealing forth strange accounts of the popular superstitions and legends of the surrounding country, with which he had become acquainted in the course of his antiquarian researches. I am half inclined to think that the old gentleman was himself somewhat tinctured with superstition, as men are very apt to be who live a recluse and studious life in a sequestered part of the country, and pore over black-letter tracts, so often filled with the marvelous and supernatural. He gave us several anecdotes of the fancies of the neighboring peasantry concerning the effigy of the crusader, which lay on the tomb by the church altar. As it was the only monument of the kind in that part of the country, it had always been regarded with feelings of superstition by the good wives of the village. It was said to get up from the tomb and walk the rounds of the churchyard in stormy nights, particularly when it thundered; and one old woman, whose cottage bordered on the churchyard, had seen it through the windows of the church, when the moon shone, slowly pacing up and down the aisles. It was the belief that some wrong had been left unredressed by the deceased, or some treasure hidden, which kept the spirit in a state of trouble and restlessness. Some talked of gold and jewels buried in the tomb, over which the specter kept watch; and there was a story current of a sexton in old times, who endeavored to break his way to the coffin at night, but, just as he reached it, received a violent blow from the marble hand of the effigy, which stretched him senseless on the pavement. These tales were often laughed at by some of the sturdier among the rustics, yet, when night came on, there were many of the stoutest unbelievers that were shy of venturing alone in the footpath that led across the churchyard.

From these and other anecdotes that followed, the crusader appeared to be the favorite hero of ghost stories throughout the vicinity. His picture, which hung up in the hall, was thought by the servants to have something supernatural about it; for they remarked, that, in whatever part of the hall you went, the eyes of the warrior were still fixed on you. The old porter's wife, too, at the lodge, who had been born and brought up in the family, and was a great gossip among the maid-servants, affirmed that in her young days she had often heard say, that on midsummer eve, when it was well known all kinds of ghosts, goblins, and fairies become visible and walk abroad, the crusader used to mount his horse, come down from his picture, ride about the house, down the avenue, and so to the church to visit the tomb, on which occasion the church door most civilly swung open of itself; not that he needed it, for he rode through closed gates and even stone walls, and had been seen by one of the dairy-maids to pass between two bars of the great park gate, making himself as thin as a sheet of paper.

All these superstitions I found had been very much countenanced by the Squire, who, though not superstitious himself, was very fond of seeing others so. He listened to every goblin tale of the neighboring gossips with infinite gravity, and held the porter's wife in high favor on account of her talent for the marvelous. He was himself a great reader of old legends and romances, and often lamented that he could not believe in them; for a superstitious person, he thought, must live in a kind of fairyland.

Whilst we were all attention to the parson's stories, our ears were suddenly assailed by a burst of heterogeneous sounds from the hall, in which were mingled something like the clang of rude minstrelsy, with the uproar of many small voices and girlish laughter. The door suddenly flew open, and a train came troop-ing into the room, that might almost have been mistaken for the breaking-up of the court of Fairy. That indefatigable spirit Master Simon, in the faithful discharge of his duties as Lord of Misrule, had conceived the idea of a Christmas mummery or masking; and having called in to his assistance the Oxonian and the young officer, who were equally ripe for anything that should occasion romping and merriment, they had carried it into instant effect. The old housekeeper had been consulted; the antique clothes-presses and wardrobes rummaged, and made to yield up the relics of finery that had not seen the light for several genera-tions. The younger part of the company had been privately con-vened from parlor and hall, and the whole had been bedizened out into a burlesque imitation of an antique mask.[1]

Master Simon led the van as Ancient Christmas, quaintly ap-pareled in a ruff, a short cloak which had very much the aspect of one of the old housekeeper's petticoats, and a hat that might have served for a village steeple, and must indubitably have figured in the days of the Covenanters.[2] From under this, his nose curved boldly forth, flushed with a frost-bitten bloom that seemed the very trophy of a December blast. He was accompanied by the blue-eyed romp, dished up as Dame Mince Pie, in the ven-erable magnificence of faded brocade, long stomacher, peaked

[1] IRVING'S NOTE. — Maskings, or mummeries, were favorite sports at Christmas in old times; and the wardrobes at halls and manor-houses were often laid under contribution to furnish dresses and fantastic disguisings. I strongly suspect Master Simon to have taken the idea of his from Ben Jon-son's Masque of Christmas.

[2] In Scottish history, the name applied to a party embracing the great ma-jority of the people, who, during the seventeenth century, bound themselves to establish and maintain the Presbyterian doctrine as the sole religion of the country.

hat, and high-heeled shoes. The young officer appeared as
Robin Hood,[1] in a sporting dress of Kendal green[2] and a for-
aging cap with a gold tassel.

The costume, to be sure, did not bear testimony to deep research, and there was an evident eye to the picturesque, natural
to a young gallant in presence of his mistress. The fair Julia
hung on his arm in a pretty rustic dress, as Maid Marian.[3] The
rest of the train had been metamorphosed in various ways,— the
girls trussed up in the finery of the ancient belles of the Bracebridge line; and the striplings bewhiskered with burnt cork, and
gravely clad in broad skirts, hanging sleeves, and full-bottomed
wigs, to represent the characters of Roast Beef, Plum Pudding,
and other worthies celebrated in ancient maskings. The whole
was under the control of the Oxonian, in the appropriate character of Misrule; and I observed that he exercised rather a mischievous sway with his wand over the smaller personages of the
pageant.

The irruption of this motley crew, with beat of drum, according
to ancient custom, was the consummation of uproar and merriment. Master Simon covered himself with glory by the state-
liness with which, as Ancient Christmas, he walked a minuet[4]
with the peerless though giggling Dame Mince Pie. It was followed by a dance from all the characters, which, from its medley
of costumes, seemed as though the old family portraits had skipped
down from their frames to join in the sport. Different centuries

[1] The famous legendary outlaw (born at Locksley, in Notts, in the reign
of Henry II., 1160). His real name was Fitzooth, and it is commonly said
he was the Earl of Huntingdon.

[2] Woolen cloth of coarse texture, called Kendal from the town of that
name in Westmoreland, England, where it was first made.

[3] A name assumed by Matilda, daughter of Robert Lord Fitzwalter, while
Robin Hood (her lover) remained in a state of outlawry.

[4] A slow, very graceful dance, performed in $\frac{3}{4}$ or $\frac{3}{8}$ time; originated, it is
said, in Poitou, France, about the middle of the seventeenth century. Its
name is from the French *menuet* (Latin. *minutus*, " small "), the steps taken
in the dance being small.

were figuring at cross hands and right and left: the dark ages were cutting pirouettes[1] and rigadoons;[2] and the days of Queen Bess jigging merrily down the middle, through a line of succeeding generations.

The worthy Squire contemplated these fantastic sports, and this resurrection of his old wardrobe, with the simple relish of childish delight. He stood chuckling, and rubbing his hands, and scarcely hearing a word the parson said, notwithstanding that the latter was discoursing most authentically on the ancient and stately dance of the pavon, or peacock, from which he conceived the minuet to be derived.[3] For my part, I was in a continual excitement from the varied scenes of whim and innocent gayety passing before me. It was inspiring to see wild-eyed Frolic and warm-hearted Hospitality breaking out from among the chills and glooms of winter, and Old Age throwing off his apathy, and catching once more the freshness of youthful enjoyment. I felt also an interest in the scene, from the consideration that these fleeting customs were posting fast into oblivion, and that this was perhaps the only family in England in which the whole of them were still punctiliously observed. There was a quaintness, too, mingled with all this revelry, that gave it a peculiar zest: it was suited to the time and place; and, as the old manor-house almost reeled with mirth and wassail, it seemed echoing back the joviality of long-departed years.

But enough of Christmas and its gambols: it is time for me to pause in this garrulity. Methinks I hear the question asked by my graver readers, "To what purpose is all this? How is the

---

1 Whirling on the tip of one foot.

2 French, *rigodon*. A dance said to have come from Provence, France. It is gay and brisk in character.

3 Sir John Hawkins, speaking of the dance called pavon, from *pavo* ("a peacock"), says, "It is a grave and majestic dance; the method of dancing it anciently was by gentlemen dressed with caps and swords, by those of the long robe in their gowns, by the peers in their mantles, and by the ladies in gowns with long trains, the motion whereof, in dancing, resembled that of a peacock." — *History of Music.*

world to be made wiser by this talk?" Alas! is there not wisdom enough extant for the instruction of the world? and if not, are there not thousands of abler pens laboring for its improvement? It is so much pleasanter to please than to instruct,— to play the companion rather than the preceptor.

What, after all, is the mite of wisdom that I could throw into the mass of knowledge, or how am I sure that my sagest deductions may be safe guides for the opinions of others? But in writing to amuse, if I fail, the only evil is in my own disappointment. If, however, I can by any lucky chance, in these days of evil, rub out one wrinkle from the brow of care, or beguile the heavy heart of one moment of sorrow; if I can now and then penetrate through the gathering film of misanthropy, prompt a benevolent view of human nature, and make my reader more in good humor with his fellow-beings and himself, — surely, surely, I shall not then have written entirely in vain.

WESTMINSTER ABBEY.[1]

ON one of those sober and rather melancholy days in the latter part of autumn, when the shadows of morning and evening almost mingle together, and throw a gloom over the decline of the year, I passed several hours in rambling about Westminster Abbey. There was something congenial to the season in the mournful magnificence of the old pile; and, as I passed its threshold, it seemed like stepping back into the regions of antiquity, and losing myself among the shades of former ages.

[1] The coronation church of the sovereigns of England from the time of Harold (1066). It occupies the site of a chapel built by Siebert in honor of St. Peter, on a slightly elevated spot rising from the marshy ground bordering the Thames. The Abbey was fifteen years in building, and was the first cruciform church in England. It contains the tombs and monuments of many of the sovereigns of Great Britain, and the memorials of England's greatest men in all walks of life.

I entered from the inner court of Westminster School,[1] through a long, low, vaulted passage, that had an almost subterranean look, being dimly lighted in one part by circular perforations in the massive walls. Through this dark avenue I had a distant view of the cloisters,[2] with the figure of an old verger[3] in his black gown, moving along their shadowy vaults, and seeming like a specter from one of the neighboring tombs. The approach to the Abbey through these gloomy monastic remains prepares the mind for its solemn contemplation. The cloister still retains something of the quiet and seclusion of former days. The gray walls are discolored by damps, and crumbling with age; a coat of hoary moss has gathered over the inscriptions of the mural monuments, and obscured the death's heads and other funeral emblems; the sharp touches of the chisel are gone from the rich tracery of the arches; the roses which adorned the keystones have lost their leafy beauty; everything bears marks of the gradual dilapidations of time, which yet has something touching and pleasing in its very decay.

The sun was pouring down a yellow autumnal ray into the square of the cloisters, beaming upon a scanty plot of grass in the center, and lighting up an angle of the vaulted passage with a kind of dusty splendor. From between the arcades the eye glanced up to a bit of blue sky or a passing cloud, and beheld the sun-gilt pinnacles of the Abbey towering into the azure heaven.

As I paced the cloisters, sometimes contemplating this mingled picture of glory and decay, and sometimes endeavoring to deci-

[1] This school was in existence in 1540, established by charter of Henry VIII. Under the reign of Mary the whole school was swept away. It was restored by Elizabeth in 1560, who gave to the college the statutes which are more or less observed to this day.

[2] Old French, *cloistre;* Latin, *claustrum.* That which shuts off; in monastic buildings, an arched passage, usually running about an interior court, and used as a place of recreation for monks.

[3] Old French, *vergier;* Latin, *virga* ("a rod"). A church officer who bore the verge or staff of office for ecclesiastical dignitaries.

pher the inscriptions on the tombstones, which formed the pavement beneath my feet, my eye was attracted to three figures,
rudely carved in relief, but nearly worn away by the footsteps of
many generations. They were the effigies of three of the early
abbots. The epitaphs were entirely effaced. The names alone
remained, having, no doubt, been renewed in later times, — Vitalis[1] (Abbas, 108?), and Gislebertus Crispinus[2] (Abbas, 1114), and
Laurentius[3] (Abbas, 1176). I remained some little while, musing over these casual relics of antiquity, thus left like wrecks
upon this distant shore of time, telling no tale but that such
beings had been and had perished; teaching no moral but the
futility of that pride which hopes still to exact homage in its
ashes, and to live in an inscription. A little longer, and even
these faint records will be obliterated, and the monument will
cease to be a memorial. Whilst I was yet looking down upon
these gravestones, I was roused by the sound of the Abbey clock,
reverberating from buttress to buttress, and echoing among the
cloisters. It is almost startling to hear this warning of departed
time sounding among the tombs, and telling the lapse of the hour,
which, like a billow, has rolled us onward towards the grave.

I pursued my walk to an arched door opening to the interior of the Abbey. On entering here, the magnitude of the

---

[1] Vitalis was a Norman. He was an abbot at Bernay in Normandy, and
was expressly sent for by the King (William the Conqueror) to govern at
Westminster. He had the character of a wise and prudent man. He died
June 19, 1082, and was interred in the south cloister.

[2] Gislebertus Crispinus (Gilbert Crispin) was a Norman of noble rank.
He was particularly famous as a sound theologist and a ready disputant.
After a long life of piety and good deeds, he died Dec. 6, 1114, and was
buried at the feet of Vitalis, his predecessor.

[3] Laurentius (or Lawrence) was educated, and resided for many years, at
St. Albans. He was chosen for Westminster Abbey about the year 1159,
through the influence of Henry II., who thought highly of him. He was a
man of talents. He was appointed by the King, the Pope, and the Arch-
bishop of Canterbury, to decide several disputed causes. He was buried in
the south walk of the cloister.

building breaks fully upon the mind, contrasted with the vaults of the cloisters. The eye gazes with wonder at clustered columns of gigantic dimensions, with arches springing from them to such an amazing height; and man wandering about their bases, shrunk into insignificance in comparison with his own handiwork. The spaciousness and gloom of this vast edifice produce a profound and mysterious awe. We step cautiously and softly about, as if fearful of disturbing the hallowed silence of the tomb; while every footfall whispers along the walls, and chatters among the sepulchers, making us more sensible of the quiet we have interrupted.

It seems as if the awful nature of the place presses down upon the soul, and hushes the beholder into noiseless reverence. We feel that we are surrounded by the congregated bones of the great men of past times, who have filled history with their deeds, and the earth with their renown. And yet it almost provokes a smile at the vanity of human ambition, to see how they are crowded together and jostled in the dust; what parsimony is observed in doling out a scanty nook, a gloomy corner, a little portion of earth, to those whom, when alive, kingdoms could not satisfy; and how many shapes and forms and artifices are devised to catch the casual notice of the passenger, and save from forgetfulness for a few short years a name which once aspired to occupy ages of the world's thought and admiration.

I passed some time in Poet's Corner,[1] which occupies an end of one of the transepts or cross aisles of the Abbey. The monuments are generally simple, for the lives of literary men afford no striking themes for the sculptor. Shakespeare[2] and Addison[3] have statues erected to their memories; but the greater part have

---

[1] The poet Chaucer, who died Oct. 25, 1400, was the first to be buried in Poet's Corner, through the royal favor of Henry IV.; but no monument was placed over him until during the reign of Edward VI., in 1551.

[2] The remains of Shakespeare (1564–1616) were never moved from Stratford, but a monument was erected in the Abbey in 1740.

[3] Addison (1672–1719) is buried in the chapel of Henry VII., in the vault

busts, medallions, and sometimes mere inscriptions. Notwithstanding the simplicity of these memorials, I have always observed that the visitors to the Abbey remain longest about
them. A kinder and fonder feeling takes place of that cold
curiosity or vague admiration with which they gaze on the splendid monuments of the great and the heroic. They linger about
these as about the tombs of friends and companions; for, indeed,
there is something of companionship between the author and the
reader. Other men are known to posterity only through the medium of history, which is continually growing faint and obscure;
but the intercourse between the author and his fellowmen is ever
new, active, and immediate. He has lived for them more than
for himself; he has sacrificed surrounding enjoyments, and shut
himself up from the delights of social life, that he might the more
intimately commune with distant minds and distant ages. Well
may the world cherish his renown; for it has been purchased,
not by deeds of violence and blood, but by the diligent dispen-
sation of pleasure. Well may posterity be grateful to his memory; for he has left it an inheritance, not of empty names and
sounding actions, but whole treasures of wisdom, bright gems of
thought, and golden veins of language.

From Poet's Corner I continued my stroll towards that part of
the Abbey which contains the sepulchers of the kings. I wandered among what once were chapels, but which are now occupied by the tombs and monuments of the great. At every turn
I met with some illustrious name, or the cognizance of some
powerful house renowned in history. As the eye darts into these
dusky chambers of death, it catches glimpses of quaint effigies,—
some kneeling in niches, as if in devotion; others stretched upon
the tombs, with hands piously pressed together; warriors in armor, as if reposing after battle; prelates with crosiers and miters;
and nobles in robes and coronets, lying, as it were, in state. In

of the House of Albemarle. A monument of him stands in the Poet's Corner, and was erected in 1808.

glancing over this scene, so strangely populous, yet where every form is so still and silent, it seems almost as if we were treading a mansion of that fabled city, where every being had been suddenly transmuted into stone.

I paused to contemplate a tomb on which lay the effigy of a knight in complete armor. A large buckler was on one arm; the hands were pressed together in supplication upon the breast; the face was almost covered by the morion; the legs were crossed, in token of the warrior's having been engaged in the holy war. It was the tomb of a crusader, — of one of those military enthusiasts who so strangely mingled religion and romance, and whose exploits form the connecting link between fact and fiction, between the history and the fairy tale. There is something extremely picturesque in the tombs of these adventurers, decorated as they are with rude armorial bearings and Gothic sculpture. They comport with the antiquated chapels in which they are generally found; and in considering them, the imagination is apt to kindle with the legendary associations, the romantic fictions, the chivalrous pomp and pageantry, which poetry has spread over the wars for the sepulcher of Christ. They are the relics of times utterly gone by, of beings passed from recollection, of customs and manners with which ours have no affinity. They are like objects from some strange and distant land, of which we have no certain knowledge, and about which all our conceptions are vague and visionary. There is something extremely solemn and awful in those effigies on Gothic tombs, extended as if in the sleep of death, or in the supplication of the dying hour. They have an effect infinitely more impressive on my feelings than the fanciful attitudes, the overwrought conceits, and allegorical groups, which abound on modern monuments. I have been struck, also, with the superiority of many of the old sepulchral inscriptions. There was a noble way, in former times, of saying things simply, and yet saying them proudly; and I do not know an epitaph that breathes a loftier consciousness of family worth and honorable lineage than one which affirms, of a noble house, that "all the brothers were brave, and all the sisters virtuous."[1]

In the opposite transept to Poet's Corner stands a monument which is among the most renowned achievements of modern art, but which to me appears horrible rather than sublime. It is the tomb of Mrs. Nightingale,[2] by Roubiliac.[3] The bottom of the monument is represented as throwing open its marble doors, and a sheeted skeleton is starting forth. The shroud is falling from his fleshless frame as he launches his dart at his victim. She is sinking into her affrighted husband's arms, who strives, with vain and frantic effort, to avert the blow. The whole is executed with terrible truth and spirit: we almost fancy we hear the gibbering yell of triumph bursting from the distended jaws of the specter. But why should we thus seek to clothe death with unnecessary terrors, and to spread horrors round the tomb of those we love? The grave should be surrounded by everything that might inspire tenderness and veneration for the dead, or that might win the living to virtue. It is the place, not of disgust and dismay, but of sorrow and meditation.

While wandering about these gloomy vaults and silent aisles, studying the records of the dead, the sound of busy existence from without occasionally reaches the ear,— the rumbling of the passing equipage, the murmur of the multitude, or perhaps the

[1] A portion of the inscription upon the tomb of " the loyal " Duke of Newcastle and the Duchess. This nobleman was one of the firmest supporters of Charles I.

[2] In memory of Joseph Gascoigne Nightingale, Esq., of Minehead, Devonshire, who died in 1752; and the Lady Elizabeth his wife, who died soon after marriage. A tradition of the Abbey records that a robber, coming into the Abbey by moonlight, was so startled by the figure as to have fled in dismay, and left his crowbar on the pavement.

[3] Roubiliac (1695-1762) was an able French sculptor, born at Lyons. He settled in London in 1720, and soon became the most popular sculptor of the time in England. His chief works in the Abbey are the monuments of Handel, Admiral Warren, Marshal Wade, Mrs. Nightingale, and the Duke of Argyll.

light laugh of pleasure. The contrast is striking with the death-like repose around; and it has a strange effect upon the feelings, thus to hear the surges of active life hurrying along, and beating against the very walls of the sepulcher.

I continued in this way to move from tomb to tomb, and from chapel to chapel. The day was gradually wearing away; the distant tread of loiterers about the Abbey grew less and less frequent; the sweet-tongued bell was summoning to evening prayer; and I saw at a distance the choristers, in their white surplices, crossing the aisle and entering the choir. I stood before the entrance to Henry VII.'s Chapel.[1] A flight of steps leads up to it, through a deep and gloomy but magnificent arch. Great gates of brass, richly and delicately wrought, turn heavily upon their hinges, as if proudly reluctant to admit the feet of common mortals into this most gorgeous of sepulchers.

On entering, the eye is astonished by the pomp of architecture, and the elaborate beauty of sculptured detail. The very walls are wrought into universal ornament, incrusted with tracery, and scooped into niches crowded with the statues of saints and martyrs. Stone seems, by the cunning labor of the chisel, to have been robbed of its weight and density, suspended aloft as if by magic, and the fretted roof achieved with the wonderful minuteness and airy security of a cobweb.

Along the sides of the chapel are the lofty stalls of the Knights of the Bath[2] richly carved of oak, though with the grotesque dec-

---

[1] Designed by Henry VII. as a burying place for himself and his successors; and he expressly enjoined in his will that none but those of royal blood should be buried there. The first to be buried there was his wife, Elizabeth of York, who died in 1503. Six years later he died, and was buried by the side of his queen, not in the raised tomb, but in the vault beneath. His effigy was completed within twenty years after his death, by Torrigiano, a Florentine sculptor.

[2] This Order of the Knights of the Bath originated, it is said, in 1399, at Henry IV.'s coronation. In the earlier coronations it had been the practice of the sovereigns to create a number of knights before they started on their procession from the Tower. These knights, being made in time of peace,

orations of Gothic architecture. On the pinnacles of the stalls are affixed the helmets and crests of the knights, with their scarfs and swords; and above them are suspended their banners, emblazoned with armorial bearings, and contrasting the splendor of gold and purple and crimson with the cold, gray fretwork of the roof. In the midst of this grand mausoleum stands the sepulcher of its founder,[1]—his effigy, with that of his queen, extended on a sumptuous tomb, and the whole surrounded by a superbly wrought brazen railing.

There is a sad dreariness in this magnificence; this strange mixture of tombs and trophies, these emblems of living and aspiring ambition, close beside mementos which show the dust and oblivion in which all must sooner or later terminate. Nothing impresses the mind with a deeper feeling of loneliness, than to tread the silent and deserted scene of former throng and pageant. On looking round on the vacant stalls of the knights and their esquires, and on the rows of dusty but gorgeous banners that were once borne before them, my imagination conjured up the scene when this hall was bright with the valor and beauty of the land, glittering with the splendor of jeweled rank and military array, alive with the tread of many feet and the hum of an admiring multitude. All had passed away: the silence of death had settled again upon the place, interrupted only by the casual chirping of birds, which had found their way into the chapel, and built their nests among its friezes and pendants,—sure signs of solitariness and desertion.

were not enrolled in any existing order, and for a long period had no special designation; but inasmuch as one of the most striking and characteristic parts of their admission was the complete ablution of their persons on the eve of their knighthood, as an emblem of the cleanliness and purity of their profession, they were called "Knights of the Bath." The King himself bathed on this occasion with them. The ceremony took place at Westminster; the bath, in the Painted or Prince's Chamber; and the vigils, either before the Confessor's shrine or in Henry VII.'s Chapel.

[1] Henry VII.

When I read the names inscribed on the banners, they were those of men scattered far and wide about the world, some tossing upon distant seas, some under arms in distant lands, some mingling in the busy intrigues of courts and cabinets, all seeking to deserve one more distinction in this mansion of shadowy honors, — the melancholy reward of a monument.

Two small aisles on each side of this chapel present a touching instance of the equality of the grave, which brings down the oppressor to a level with the oppressed, and mingles the dust of the bitterest enemies together. In one is the sepulcher of the haughty Elizabeth:[1] in the other is that of her victim, the lovely and unfortunate Mary.[2] Not an hour in the day but some ejaculation of pity is uttered over the fate of the latter, mingled with indignation at her oppressor. The walls of Elizabeth's sepulcher continually echo with the sighs of sympathy heaved at the grave of her rival.

A peculiar melancholy reigns over the aisle where Mary lies buried. The light struggles dimly through windows darkened by dust. The greater part of the place is in deep shadow, and the walls are stained and tinted by time and weather. A marble figure of Mary is stretched upon the tomb, round which is an iron railing. much corroded, bearing her national emblem, — the thistle.[3] I was weary with wandering, and sat down to rest myself

[1] Elizabeth (born in 1533) reigned as Queen of England from 1558 to 1603, when she died. She was the last of the Tudors, and was called " the lion-hearted Elizabeth."

[2] Mary Queen of Scots, daughter of James V. of Scotland, was born in 1542. She was charged by Queen Elizabeth with having entered into a conspiracy against the life of the latter, and ordered to be executed. Queen Elizabeth signed the death warrant on the 1st of February, 1587; and on the morning of the 8th of February, Mary Queen of Scots, protesting her innocence, was beheaded. James I., the son of Mary, had her body taken from the Cathedral Church of Peterborough, and a monument erected over her in Westminster Abbey.

[3] The thistle, which gives name to the Scottish order, is also an heraldic bearing in that country.

by the monument, revolving in my mind the checkered and disastrous story of poor Mary.

The sound of casual footsteps had ceased from the Abbey. I could only hear now and then the distant voice of the priest repeating the evening service, and the faint responses of the choir. These paused for a time, and all was hushed. The stillness, the desertion and obscurity, that were gradually prevailing around, gave a deeper and more solemn interest to the place:

> For in the silent grave no conversation,
> No joyful tread of friends, no voice of lovers,
> No careful father's counsel, — nothing's heard,
> For nothing is, but all oblivion,
> Dust and an endless darkness.

Suddenly the notes of the deep-laboring organ burst upon the ear, falling with doubled and redoubled intensity, and rolling, as it were, huge billows of sound. How well do their volume and grandeur accord with this mighty building! With what pomp do they swell through its vast vaults, and breathe their awful harmony through these caves of death, and make the silent sepulcher vocal! And now they rise in triumph and acclamation, heaving higher and higher their accordant notes, and piling sound on sound. And now they pause, and the soft voices of the choir break out into sweet gushes of melody: they soar aloft and warble along the roof, and seem to play about these lofty vaults like the pure airs of heaven. Again the pealing organ heaves its thrilling thunders, compressing air into music, and rolling it forth upon the soul. What long-drawn cadences! What solemn sweeping concords! It grows more and more dense and powerful; it fills the vast pile, and seems to jar the very walls; the ear is stunned; the senses are overwhelmed. And now it is winding up in full jubilee. It is rising from the earth to heaven. The very soul seems rapt away and floated upwards on this swelling tide of harmony.

I sat for some time lost in that kind of reverie which a strain of music is apt sometimes to inspire. The shadows of evening were gradually thickening around me, the monuments began to cast deeper and deeper gloom, and the distant clock again gave token of the slowly waning day.

I rose, and prepared to leave the Abbey. As I descended the flight of steps which lead into the body of the building, my eye was caught by the shrine[1] of Edward the Confessor; and I ascended the small staircase that conducts to it, to take from thence a general survey of this wilderness of tombs. The shrine is elevated upon a kind of platform, and close around it are the sepulchers of various kings and queens. From this eminence the eye looks down between pillars and funeral trophies to the chapels and chambers below, crowded with tombs, where warriors, prelates, courtiers, and statesmen lie moldering in their "beds of darkness." Close by me stood the great chair of coronation,[2] rudely carved of oak, in the barbarous taste of a remote and Gothic age. The scene seemed almost as if contrived, with theatrical artifice, to produce an effect upon the beholder. Here was a type of the beginning and the end of human pomp and power: here it was literally but a step from the throne to the sepulcher. Would not one think that these incongruous mementos had been gathered together as a lesson to living greatness?— to show it, even in the moment of its proudest exaltation, the neglect and dishonor to which it must soon arrive; how soon that crown which encircles its brow must pass away, and it must lie down in the dust and disgraces of the tomb, and be trampled

[1] Erected by Henry III. on the canonizing of Edward, King of England, by Pope Alexander III., who caused his name to be placed in the catalogue of saints. The shrine was the work of the Italian artist Cavallini. This shrine was a constant object of pilgrimages from all parts of England all through the middle ages.

[2] This chair must have been specially constructed for the reception of the famous stone which Edward I. brought from Scotland in 1296. It has been constantly used at coronations ever since. The coronation takes place while the sovereign is seated in the chair. The last time it was brought out from the chapel where it stands was at the Jubilee Thanksgiving service (1888), when the Queen sat in it during the ceremonial.

upon by the feet of the meanest of the multitude: for, strange to tell, even the grave is here no longer a sanctuary. There is a shocking levity in some natures, which leads them to sport with awful and hallowed things; and there are base minds, which delight to revenge on the illustrious dead the abject homage and groveling servility which they pay to the living. The coffin of Edward the Confessor has been broken open, and his remains despoiled of their funeral ornaments; the scepter has been stolen from the hand of the imperious Elizabeth; and the effigy of Henry V. lies headless.[1] Not a royal monument but bears some proof how false and fugitive is the homage of mankind. Some are plundered, some mutilated, some covered with ribaldry and insult, all more or less outraged and dishonored.

The last beams of day were now faintly streaming through the painted windows in the high vaults above me. The lower parts of the Abbey were already wrapped in the obscurity of twilight. The chapels and aisles grew darker and darker. The effigies of the kings faded into shadows; the marble figures of the monuments assumed strange shapes in the uncertain light; the evening breeze crept through the aisles like the cold breath of the grave; and even the distant footfall of a verger, traversing the Poet's Corner, had something strange and dreary in its sound. I slowly retraced my morning's walk; and as I passed out at the portal of the cloisters, the door, closing with a jarring noise behind me, filled the whole building with echoes.

I endeavored to form some arrangement in my mind of the objects I had been contemplating, but found they were already falling into indistinctness and confusion. Names, inscriptions, trophies, had all become confounded in my recollection, though I had scarcely taken my foot from off the threshold. What, thought I, is this vast assemblage of sepulchers, but a treasury of

---

[1] The effigy is said to have originally been plated with silver, and the *head* to have been of solid silver. Nothing is now left but the wooden form upon which the gilded plates were fastened. Henry V. was King of England from 1413 to 1422.

humiliation, — a huge pile of reiterated homilies on the emptiness of renown and the certainty of oblivion? It is, indeed, the empire of Death; his great, shadowy palace, where he sits in state, mocking at the relics of human glory, and spreading dust and forgetfulness on the monuments of princes. How idle a boast, after all, is the immortality of a name! Time is ever silently turning over his pages. We are too much engrossed by the story of the present to think of the characters and anecdotes that gave interest to the past; and each age is a volume thrown aside to be speedily forgotten. The idol of to-day pushes the hero of yesterday out of our recollection, and will, in turn, be supplanted by his successor of to-morrow. "Our fathers," says Sir Thomas Brown,[1] "find their graves in our short memories, and sadly tell us how we may be buried in our survivors." History fades into fable, fact becomes clouded with doubt and controversy, the inscription molders from the tablet, the statue falls from the pedestal. Columns, arches, pyramids — what are they but heaps of sand, and their epitaphs but characters written in the dust? What is the security of the tomb, or the perpetuity of an embalmment? The remains of Alexander the Great[2] have been scattered to the wind, and his empty sarcophagus is now the mere curiosity of a museum. "The Egyptian mummies, which Cambyses[3] or

---

[1] A distinguished English writer, born in London in 1605. He graduated at Oxford in 1626; studied medicine and practiced in Oxfordshire, and received the degree of M.D. at the University of Leyden. He published a work, Religio Medici, which was a success, and he became celebrated as a man of letters. In 1671 he was made a knight by Charles II.

[2] Alexander III. (commonly called "the Great") was born at Pella, 356 B.C. He was a great warrior, and successful in all his exploits, conquering all the world then known. He died after a reign of less than thirteen years, and before he had reached the age of thirty-three.

[3] The elder son and successor of Cyrus, who reigned over the Persian Empire for seven years and five months (529–521 B.C.). He made a conquest of Egypt in 525 B.C. He assumed the responsibilities and titles proper to a king of Egypt, taking as his throne name that of "Kambath-Remesot, Lord of Upper and Lower Egypt."

time hath spared, avarice now consumeth. Mizraim[1] cures wounds, and Pharaoh[2] is sold for balsams."[3]

What, then, is to insure this pile which now towers above me from sharing the fate of mightier mausoleums? The time must come when its gilded vaults, which now spring so loftily, shall lie in rubbish beneath the feet; when, instead of the sound of melody and praise, the wind shall whistle through the broken arches, and the owl hoot from the shattered tower; when the garish sunbeam shall break into these gloomy mansions of death, and the ivy twine round the fallen column, and the fox-glove hang its blossoms about the nameless urn as if in mockery of the dead. Thus man passes away; his name perishes from record and recollection; his history is as a tale that is told; and his very monument becomes a ruin.

THE LEGEND OF SLEEPY HOLLOW.

[*Found among the Papers of the Late Diedrich Knickerbocker.*]

"*A pleasing land of drowsy head it was,*
Of dreams that wave before the half-shut eye,
And of gay castles in the clouds that pass,
Forever flushing round a summer sky."

CASTLE OF INDOLENCE.[4]

IN the bosom of one of those spacious coves which indent the eastern shore of the Hudson, at that broad expansion of the river denominated by the ancient Dutch navigators the Tappan

---

1 Mizraim, or Mizri, is the Hebrew name for Egypt.

2 The title of Pharaoh was applied to the kings of Egypt, from Menes to Solomon.

3 From Sir T. Brown. In the sixteenth and part of the seventeenth centuries, mummy formed one of the ordinary drugs, and was found in the shops of all the apothecaries. Tombs were searched, and as many mummies as could be obtained were broken into pieces for the purpose of sale. Physicians of all nations commonly prescribed it in cases of bruises and wounds.

4 James Thomson (1700–48) was the son of a Scotch minister, and author

Zee,[1] and where they always prudently shortened sail, and implored the protection of St. Nicholas[2] when they crossed, there lies a small market town or rural port, which by some is called Greensburgh, but which is more generally and properly known by the name of "Tarrytown."[3] This name was given it, we are told, in former days, by the good housewives of the adjacent country, from the inveterate propensity of their husbands to linger about the village tavern on market days. Be that as it may, I do not vouch for the fact, but merely advert to it for the sake of being precise and authentic. Not far from this village, perhaps about three miles, there is a little valley, or rather lap of land, among high hills, which is one of the quietest places in the whole world. A small brook glides through it, with just murmur enough to lull one to repose; and the occasional whistle of a quail, or tapping of a woodpecker, is almost the only sound that ever breaks in upon the uniform tranquillity.

I recollect, that, when a stripling, my first exploit in squirrel-shooting was in a grove of tall walnut-trees that shades one side of the valley. I had wandered into it at noontime, when all nature is peculiarly quiet, and was startled by the roar of my own gun, as it broke the sabbath stillness around, and was prolonged and reverberated by the angry echoes. If ever I should wish for a retreat, whither I might steal from the world and its distrac-

---

of The Seasons, which gave him a great reputation. The Castle of Indolence, from which the above verse is quoted, was his last work, and was published the year he died. Till the advent of Scott and Byron, Thomson was the most widely popular poet in our language.

[1] The expansion of the Hudson River between Haverstraw and Piermont, having a length of about twelve miles, and a breadth in the neighborhood of from four to five miles.

[2] Bishop of Myra in the fourth century. He was also the mariner's saint, and is the present patron of those who lead a seafaring life (as Neptune was of old).

[3] Tarrytown is twenty-seven miles from New York. It is famous both historically and from its connection with Washington Irving, whose cottage, "Sunnyside," is in the vicinity.

tions, and dream quietly away the remnant of a troubled life, I know of none more promising than this little valley.

From the listless repose of the place, and the peculiar character of its inhabitants, who are descendants from the original Dutch settlers, this sequestered glen has long been known by the name of "Sleepy Hollow," and its rustic lads are called the "Sleepy Hollow Boys" throughout all the neighboring country. A drowsy, dreamy influence seems to hang over the land, and to pervade the very atmosphere. Some say that the place was bewitched by a high German doctor during the early days of the settlement; others, that an old Indian chief, the prophet or wizard of his tribe, held his powwows there before the country was discovered by Master Hendrick Hudson.[1] Certain it is, the place still continues under the sway of some witching power, that holds a spell over the minds of the good people, causing them to walk in a continual reverie. They are given to all kinds of marvelous beliefs; are subject to trances and visions; and frequently see strange sights, and hear music and voices in the air. The whole neighborhood abounds with local tales, haunted spots, and twilight superstitions; stars shoot and meteors glare oftener across the valley than in any other part of the country; and the nightmare, with her whole ninefold,[2] seems to make it the favorite scene of her gambols.

The dominant spirit, however, that haunts this enchanted region, and seems to be commander-in-chief of all the powers of the air, is the apparition of a figure on horseback without a head. It is said by some to be the ghost of a Hessian[3] trooper, whose

---

[1] A distinguished English navigator, who made four voyages, attempting to find a shorter passage to China than by the way of the Cape of Good Hope. On the third of these voyages he entered the bay now called New York Bay, and (Sept. 11, 1609) sailed up what is now the Hudson River. During his fourth voyage, two years later, he penetrated the straits and discovered the great bay of Canada which now bears his name. Here his mutinous sailors cast him adrift in a small boat, and left him to die.

[2] See King Lear, act iii. sc. 4.

[3] These Hessians came from a province of western Germany called Hesse

head had been carried away by a cannon-ball in some nameless battle during the Revolutionary war, and who is ever and anon seen by the country folk hurrying along in the gloom of night, as if on the wings of the wind. His haunts are not confined to the valley, but extend at times to the adjacent roads, and especially to the vicinity of a church that is at no great distance. Indeed, certain of the most authentic historians of those parts, who have been careful in collecting and collating the floating facts concerning this specter, allege that, the body of the trooper having been buried in the churchyard, the ghost rides forth to the scene of battle in nightly quest of his head; and that the rushing speed with which he sometimes passes along the hollow, like a midnight blast, is owing to his being belated, and in a hurry to get back to the churchyard before daybreak.

Such is the general purport of this legendary superstition, which has furnished materials for many a wild story in that region of shadows; and the specter is known at all the country firesides by the name of "The Headless Horseman of Sleepy Hollow."

It is remarkable that the visionary propensity I have mentioned is not confined to the native inhabitants of the valley, but is unconsciously imbibed by every one who resides there for a time. However wide-awake they may have been before they entered that sleepy region, they are sure, in a little time, to inhale the witching influence of the air, and begin to grow imaginative, — to dream dreams, and see apparitions.

I mention this peaceful spot with all possible laud: for it is in such little retired Dutch valleys, found here and there embosomed in the great State of New York, that population, manners, and customs remain fixed; while the great torrent of migration and improvement, which is making such incessant changes in other parts of this restless country, sweeps by them

Cassel. They were brought to America by the British in 1776, having been hired by them to fight against the American troops.

unobserved.   They are like those little nooks of still water which border a rapid stream, where we may see the straw and bubble riding quietly at anchor, or slowly revolving in their mimic harbor, undisturbed by the rush of the passing current.   Though many years have elapsed since I trod the drowsy shades of Sleepy Hollow, yet I question whether I should not still find the same trees and the same families vegetating in its sheltered bosom.

In this by-place of Nature there abode, in a remote period of American history, — that is to say, some thirty years since, — a worthy wight of the name of Ichabod Crane, who sojourned, or, as he expressed it, "tarried," in Sleepy Hollow, for the purpose of instructing the children of the vicinity.   He was a native of Connecticut, — a State which supplies the Union with pioneers for the mind as well as for the forest, and sends forth yearly its legions of frontier woodmen and country schoolmasters.   The cognomen of Crane was not inapplicable to his person.   He was tall, but exceedingly lank, with narrow shoulders, long arms and legs, hands that dangled a mile out of his sleeves, feet that might have served for shovels, and his whole frame most loosely hung together.   His head was small, and flat at top, with huge ears, large green glassy eyes, and a long snipe nose, so that it looked like a weathercock perched upon his spindle neck to tell which way the wind blew.   To see him striding along the profile of a hill on a windy day, with his clothes bagging and fluttering about him, one might have mistaken him for the genius of famine descending upon the earth, or some scarecrow eloped from a cornfield.

His schoolhouse was a low building of one large room, rudely constructed of logs; the windows partly glazed, and partly patched with leaves of old copy-books.   It was most ingeniously secured at vacant hours by a withe twisted in the handle of the door, and stakes set against the window-shutters; so that, though a thief might get in with perfect ease, he would find some embarrassment in getting out, — an idea most probably borrowed by the architect, Yost Van Houten, from the mystery of an eel-pot.[1]   The schoolhouse stood in a rather lonely but pleasant situation, just at the foot of a woody hill, with a brook running close by, and a formidable birch-tree growing at one end of it. From hence the low murmur of his pupils' voices, conning over their lessons, might be heard of a drowsy summer's day, like the hum of a beehive ; interrupted now and then by the authoritative voice of the master in the tone of menace or command, or, per-adventure, by the appalling sound of the birch as he urged some tardy loiterer along the flowery path of knowledge.   Truth to say, he was a conscientious man, that ever bore in mind the golden maxim, " Spare the rod and spoil the child."[2]   Ichabod Crane's scholars certainly were not spoiled.

I would not have it imagined, however, that he was one of those cruel potentates of the school who joy in the smart of their subjects : on the contrary, he administered justice with discrimination rather than severity ; taking the burthen off the backs of the weak, and laying it on those of the strong.   Your mere puny stripling, that winced at the least flourish of the rod, was passed by with indulgence ; but the claims of justice were satisfied by inflicting a double portion on some little, tough, wrong-headed, broad-skirted Dutch urchin, who sulked and swelled and grew dogged and sullen beneath the birch.   All this he called " doing his duty by their parents ;" and he never inflicted a chastisement without following it by the assurance, so consolatory to the smart-ing urchin, that " he would remember it and thank him for it the longest day he had to live."

When school hours were over, he was even the companion and playmate of the larger boys, and on holiday afternoons would convoy some of the smaller ones home, who happened to have pretty sisters, or good housewives for mothers, noted for the

[1] A box or basket for catching eels.   The only opening is at the bottom of a funnel-shaped entrance, and is so small and so located, that, having entered it, the eels cannot easily find it again in order to get out.

[2] King Solomon's.

comforts of the cupboard.   Indeed, it behooved him to keep on
good terms with his pupils.   The revenue arising from his school
was small, and would have been scarcely sufficient to furnish him
with daily bread, for he was a huge feeder, and, though lank,
had the dilating powers of an anaconda;[1] but to help out his
maintenance, he was, according to country custom in those parts,
boarded and lodged at the houses of the farmers whose children
he instructed.   With these he lived successively a week at a time;
thus going the rounds of the neighborhood, with all his worldly
effects tied up in a cotton handkerchief.

That all this might not be too onerous on the purses of his
rustic patrons, who are apt to consider the costs of schooling a
grievous burthen, and schoolmasters as mere drones, he had various ways of rendering himself both useful and agreeable.   He
assisted the farmers occasionally in the lighter labors of their
farms, helped to make hay, mended the fences, took the horses to
water, drove the cows from pasture, and cut wood for the winter
fire.   He laid aside, too, all the dominant dignity and absolute
sway with which he lorded it in his little empire the school, and
became wonderfully gentle and ingratiating.   He found favor in
the eyes of the mothers by petting the children, particularly the
youngest; and like "the lion bold," which whilom so magnani-
mously "the lamb did hold,"[2] he would sit with a child on one
knee, and rock a cradle with his foot for whole hours together.

In addition to his other vocations, he was the singing-master
of the neighborhood, and picked up many bright shillings by
instructing the young folks in psalmody.   It was a matter of no
little vanity to him on Sundays, to take his station in front of the

---

[1] A reptile possessing extraordinary powers of dilation.   It kills by con-
striction.

[2] The New England Primer, published in Walpole, N.H., in 1814, contains an illustrated alphabet.   The letter *L* is illustrated by a lion with one
of its paws resting upon a lamb which is lying down, and the following
lines : —

> "The Lion bold
> The Lamb doth hold."

church gallery with a band of chosen singers, where, in his own mind, he completely carried away the palm from the parson.[1] Certain it is, his voice resounded far above all the rest of the congregation; and there are peculiar quavers still to be heard in that church, and which may even be heard half a mile off, quite to the opposite side of the mill-pond, on a still Sunday morning, which are said to be legitimately descended from the nose of Ichabod Crane. Thus, by divers little makeshifts in that ingenious way which is commonly denominated "by hook and by crook,"[2] the worthy pedagogue got on tolerably enough, and was thought, by all who understood nothing of the labor of headwork, to have a wonderfully easy life of it.

The schoolmaster is generally a man of some importance in the female circle of a rural neighborhood, being considered a kind of idle, gentlemanlike personage, of vastly superior taste and accomplishments to the rough country swains, and, indeed, inferior in learning only to the parson. His appearance, therefore, is apt to occasion some little stir at the tea-table of a farmhouse, and the addition of a supernumerary dish of cakes or sweet-meats, or, peradventure, the parade of a silver teapot. Our man of letters, therefore, was peculiarly happy in the smiles of all the country damsels. How he would figure among them in the churchyard, between services on Sundays! gathering grapes for them from the wild vines that overrun the surrounding trees; reciting for their amusement all the epitaphs on the tombstones; or sauntering with a whole bevy of them along the banks of the adjacent mill-pond; while the more bashful country bumpkins hung sheepishly back, envying his superior elegance and address.

From his half itinerant life, also, he was a kind of traveling

---

[1] Surpassed the parson in point of excellence.

[2] Formerly the poor of a manor were allowed to go into the forests with a hook and crook to get wood. What they could not reach, they might pull down with their crook. This sort of living was very precarious, but eagerly sought. Boundary stones, beyond which " the hook and crook folk " might not pass, exist still.

gazette, carrying the whole budget of local gossip from house to
house; so that his appearance was always greeted with satisfac-
tion. He was, moreover, esteemed by the women as a man of
great erudition, for he had read several books quite through, and
was a perfect master of Cotton Mather's[1] "History of New England Witchcraft;" in which, by the way, he most firmly and
potently believed.

He was, in fact, an odd mixture of small shrewdness and simple credulity. His appetite for the marvelous, and his powers
of digesting it, were equally extraordinary; and both had been
increased by his residence in this spell-bound region. No tale
was too gross or monstrous for his capacious swallow. It was
often his delight, after his school was dismissed in the afternoon,
to stretch himself on the rich bed of clover bordering the little
brook that whimpered by his schoolhouse, and there con over
old Mather's direful tales, until the gathering dusk of evening
made the printed page a mere mist before his eyes. Then, as he
wended his way, by swamp and stream and awful woodland, to
the farmhouse where he happened to be quartered, every sound
of Nature, at that witching hour, fluttered his excited imagination,
— the moan of the whip-poor-will[2] from the hillside; the boding
cry of the tree-toad, that harbinger of storm; the dreary hooting
of the screech-owl; or the sudden rustling in the thicket of birds
frightened from their roost. The fire-flies, too, which sparkled
most vividly in the darkest places, now and then startled him, as
one of uncommon brightness would stream across his path; and
if by chance a huge blockhead of a beetle came winging his

---

[1] A celebrated theologian and writer, born in Boston in 1663. He was
ordained as a minister in 1684, and preached in Boston. From the first he
was eager to bring to trial and punishment those supposed to be guilty of
witchcraft; and, when others began clearly to see the folly and injustice of
these cruel persecutions, he earnestly, though vainly, strove to stem the reac-
tion in the popular mind.

[2] A whip-poor-will is a bird which is only heard at night. It receives its
name from its note, which is thought to resemble those words.

blundering flight against him, the poor varlet was ready to give up the ghost, with the idea that he was struck with a witch's token. His only resource on such occasions, either to drown thought or drive away evil spirits, was to sing psalm tunes; and the good people of Sleepy Hollow, as they sat by their doors of an evening, were often filled with awe at hearing his nasal melody, " in linked sweetness long drawn out," [1] floating from the distant hill or along the dusky road.

Another of his sources of fearful pleasure was to pass long winter evenings with the old Dutch wives, as they sat spinning by the fire, with a row of apples roasting and sputtering along the hearth, and listen to their marvelous tales of ghosts and goblins, and haunted fields, and haunted brooks, and haunted bridges, and haunted houses, and particularly of the headless horseman, or " Galloping Hessian of the Hollow," as they sometimes called him. He would delight them equally by his anecdotes of witchcraft, and of the direful omens and portentous sights and sounds in the air, which prevailed in the earlier times of Connecticut, [2] and would frighten them wofully with speculations upon comets and shooting stars, and with the alarming fact that the world did absolutely turn round, and that they were half the time topsy-turvy.

But if there was a pleasure in all this, while snugly cuddling in the chimney corner of a chamber that was all of a ruddy glow from the crackling wood fire, and where, of course, no specter dared to show its face, it was dearly purchased by the terrors of his subsequent walk homewards. What fearful shapes and shadows beset his path amidst the dim and ghastly glare of a snowy night! With what wistful look did he eye every trembling ray of light streaming across the waste fields from some dis-

---

[1] From Milton's L'Allegro.

[2] In New England, in 1692, many people believed in witches. Such firm believers were they in witchcraft, that it was very easy to create a suspicion against a person as a witch. Many were thrown into prison, and some were hanged, in consequence.

tant window! How often was he appalled by some shrub covered with snow, which, like a sheeted specter, beset his very
path! How often did he shrink with curdling awe at the sound
of his own steps on the frosty crust beneath his feet, and dread
to look over his shoulder, lest he should behold some uncouth
being tramping close behind him! and how often was he thrown
into complete dismay by some rushing blast, howling among the
trees, in the idea that it was the Galloping Hessian on one of his
nightly scourings!

All these, however, were mere terrors of the night, phantoms
of the mind that walk in darkness; and though he had seen
many specters in his time, and been more than once beset by
Satan in divers shapes in his lonely perambulations, yet daylight
put an end to all these evils; and he would have passed a pleasant life of it, in despite of the Devil and all his works, if his path
had not been crossed by a being that causes more perplexity to
mortal man than ghosts, goblins, and the whole race of witches
put together, and that was — a woman.

Among the musical disciples who assembled one evening in
each week to receive his instructions in psalmody, was Katrina
Van Tassel, the daughter and only child of a substantial Dutch
farmer. She was a blooming lass of fresh eighteen; plump as a
partridge; ripe and melting and rosy-cheeked as one of her
father's peaches; and universally famed, not merely for her
beauty, but her vast expectations. She was, withal, a little of a
coquette, as might be perceived even in her dress, which was a
mixture of ancient and modern fashions, as most suited to set off
her charms. She wore the ornaments of pure yellow gold which
her great-great-grandmother had brought over from Saardam;[1]
the tempting stomacher of the olden time; and, withal, a pro-
vokingly short petticoat, to display the prettiest foot and ankle
in the country round.

[1] Zaandam, Zaanredam, or Saardam, is a village of Holland in the province of North Holland, five miles by rail from Amsterdam. Peter the Great
of Russia wrought at Saardam as a ship carpenter in 1697.

Ichabod Crane had a soft and foolish heart towards the sex; and it is not to be wondered at that so tempting a morsel soon found favor in his eyes, more especially after he had visited her in her paternal mansion. Old Baltus Van Tassel was a perfect picture of a thriving, contented, liberal-hearted farmer. He seldom, it is true, sent either his eyes or his thoughts beyond the boundaries of his own farm; but within these everything was snug, happy, and well-conditioned. He was satisfied with his wealth, but not proud of it, and piqued himself upon the hearty abundance rather than the style in which he lived. His stronghold was situated on the banks of the Hudson, in one of those green, sheltered, fertile nooks in which the Dutch farmers are so fond of nestling. A great elm-tree spread its broad branches over it, at the foot of which bubbled up a spring of the softest and sweetest water in a little well formed of a barrel, and then stole sparkling away through the grass to a neighboring brook that babbled along among alders and dwarf willows. Hard by the farmhouse was a vast barn that might have served for a church, every window and crevice of which seemed bursting forth with the treasures of the farm. The flail was busily resounding within it from morning to night; swallows and martins skimmed twittering about the eaves; and rows of pigeons — some with one eye turned up, as if watching the weather; some with their heads under their wings or buried in their bosoms; and others swelling, and cooing, and bowing about their dames — were enjoying the sunshine on the roof. Sleek, unwieldy porkers were grunting in the repose and abundance of their pens; from whence sallied forth, now and then, troops of sucking pigs, as if to snuff the air. A stately squadron of snowy geese were riding in an adjoining pond, convoying whole fleets of ducks. Regiments of turkeys were gobbling through the farmyard, and guinea-fowls fretting about it like ill-tempered housewives, with their peevish, discontented cry. Before the barn door strutted the gallant cock, that pattern of a husband, a warrior, and a fine gentleman, clapping his burnished wings and crowing in the pride and gladness of his heart, sometimes tearing up the earth with his feet, and then generously calling his ever-hungry family of wives and children to enjoy the rich morsel which he had discovered.

The pedagogue's mouth watered as he looked upon this sumptuous promise of luxurious winter fare. In his devouring mind's eye he pictured to himself every roasting pig running about " with a pudding in its belly "[1] and an apple in its mouth; the pigeons were snugly put to bed in a comfortable pie, and tucked in with a coverlet of crust; the geese were swimming in their own gravy; and the ducks pairing cosily in dishes, like snug married couples, with a decent competency of onion sauce. In the porkers he saw carved out the future sleek side of bacon, and juicy, relishing ham; not a turkey but he beheld daintily trussed up, with its gizzard under its wing, and, peradventure, a necklace of savory sausages; and even bright chanticleer[2] himself lay sprawling on his back, in a side-dish, with uplifted claws, as if craving that quarter which his chivalrous spirit disdained to ask while living.

As the enraptured Ichabod fancied all this, and as he rolled his great green eyes over the fat meadow-lands, the rich fields of wheat, of rye, of buckwheat and Indian corn, and the orchards burthened with ruddy fruit, which surrounded the warm tenement of Van Tassel, his heart yearned after the damsel who was to inherit these domains; and his imagination expanded with the idea, how they might be readily turned into cash, and the money invested in immense tracts of wild land, and shingle palaces in the wilderness. Nay, his busy fancy already realized his hopes, and presented to him the blooming Katrina, with a whole family of children, mounted on the top of a wagon loaded with household

---

[1] From Shakespeare, Henry IV., Part I. act ii. sc. 4.

[2] A cock. Old French, *chantecler* (from *chanter*, " to sing;" and *cler*, " clear"), the name of the cock in the poem Reynard the Fox. The Middle English forms of the word were *chauntecleer, chaunteclere, chanteclere.* Compare Chaucer, Nun's Priest's Tale, l. 501: " This chauntecleer his wynges gan to bete."

trumpery, with pots and kettles dangling beneath; and he beheld himself bestriding a pacing mare, with a colt at her heels, setting out for Kentucky, Tennessee, or the Lord knows where.

When he entered the house, the conquest of his heart was complete. It was one of those spacious farmhouses, with high-ridged but lowly-sloping roofs, built in the style handed down from the first Dutch settlers; the low, projecting eaves forming a piazza along the front, capable of being closed up in bad weather. Under this were hung flails, harness, various utensils of husbandry, and nets for fishing in the neighboring river. Benches were built along the sides for summer use; and a great spinning-wheel at one end, and a churn at the other, showed the various uses to which this important porch might be devoted. From this piazza the wonderful Ichabod entered the hall, which formed the center of the mansion, and the place of usual residence. Here rows of resplendent pewter, ranged on a long dresser, dazzled his eyes. In one corner stood a huge bag of wool ready to be spun; in another, a quantity of linsey-woolsey[1] just from the loom. Ears of Indian corn, and strings of dried apples and peaches, hung in gay festoons along the walls, mingled with the gaud of red peppers: and a door left ajar gave him a peep into the best parlor, where the claw-footed chairs and dark mahogany tables shone like mirrors; andirons, with their accompanying shovel and tongs, glistened from their covert of asparagus tops; mock-oranges and conch-shells decorated the mantelpiece; strings of various colored bird's eggs were suspended above it; a great ostrich egg was hung from the center of the room; and a corner cupboard, knowingly left open, displayed immense treasures of old silver and well-mended china.

From the moment Ichabod laid his eyes upon these regions of delight, the peace of his mind was at an end, and his only study was how to gain the affections of the peerless daughter of Van Tassel. In this enterprise, however, he had more real difficulties

---

[1] Coarse cloth, having a linen warp and a woolen woof.

than generally fell to the lot of a knight-errant[1] of yore, who sel.
dom had anything but giants, enchanters, fiery dragons, and such-
like easily conquered adversaries to contend with; and had to
make his way merely through gates of iron and brass, and walls
of adamant, to the castle keep, where the lady of his heart was
confined,— all which he achieved as easily as a man would carve
his way to the center of a Christmas pie, and then the lady gave
him her hand as a matter of course. Ichabod, on the contrary,
had to win his way to the heart of a country coquette, beset with
a labyrinth of whims and caprices, which were forever presenting new difficulties and impediments; and he had to encounter a
host of fearful adversaries of real flesh and blood, the numerous
rustic admirers, who beset every portal to her heart, keeping a
watchful and angry eye upon each other, but ready to fly out in
the common cause against any new competitor.

Among these the most formidable was a burly, roaring, roys-
tering blade, of the name of Abraham, or, according to the Dutch
abbreviation, Brom Van Brunt, the hero of the country round,
which rang with his feats of strength and hardihood. He was
broad-shouldered and double-jointed, with short, curly black hair,
and a bluff but not unpleasant countenance, having a mingled air
of fun and arrogance. From his Herculean frame and great powers of limb, he had received the nickname of " Brom Bones," by
which he was universally known. He was famed for great knowledge and skill in horsemanship, being as dexterous on horseback
as a Tartar.[2] He was foremost at all races and cock-fights, and,
with the ascendency which bodily strength always acquires in
rustic life, was the umpire in all disputes, setting his hat on one
side, and giving his decisions with an air and tone that admitted
of no gainsay or appeal. He was always ready for either a fight
or a frolic; had more mischief than ill will in his composition;
and, with all his overbearing roughness, there was a strong dash

[1] A knight who wandered in search of adventure.
[2] The Tartars were a nomadic tribe of Central Asia, noted for their fine
horsemanship.

of waggish good-humor at bottom. He had three or four boon companions of his own stamp, who regarded him as their model, and at the head of whom he scoured the country, attending every scene of feud or merriment for miles around. In cold weather he was distinguished by a fur cap, surmounted with a flaunting fox's tail; and when the folks at a country gathering descried this well-known crest at a distance, whisking about among a squad of hard riders, they always stood by for a squall. Sometimes his crew would be heard dashing along past the farmhouses at midnight, with whoop and halloo, like a troop of Don Cossacks;[1] and the old dames, startled out of their sleep, would listen for a moment till the hurry-scurry had clattered by, and then exclaim, "Ay, there goes Brom Bones and his gang!" The neighbors looked upon him with a mixture of awe, admiration, and good will, and, when any madcap prank or rustic brawl occurred in the vicinity, always shook their heads, and warranted Brom Bones was at the bottom of it.

This rantipole[2] hero had for some time singled out the blooming Katrina for the object of his uncouth gallantries, and though his amorous toyings were something like the gentle caresses and endearments of a bear, yet it was whispered that she did not altogether discourage his hopes. Certain it is, his advances were signals for rival candidates to retire, who felt no inclination to cross a lion in his amours; insomuch, that when his horse was seen tied to Van Tassel's paling on a Sunday night, — a sure sign that his master was courting, or, as it is termed, "sparking," within, — all other suitors passed by in despair, and carried the war into other quarters.

Such was the formidable rival with whom Ichabod Crane had to contend; and, considering all things, a stouter man than he would have shrunk from the competition, and a wiser man would

[1] The Russian tribes who settled on the River Don. They are a restless and warlike race. They form a first-rate irregular cavalry, and render excellent service as scouts and skirmishers.

[2] Wild.

have despaired. He had, however, a happy mixture of pliability and perseverance in his nature. He was in form and spirit like a supple-jack, — yielding, but tough; though he bent, he never broke; and though he bowed beneath the slightest pressure, yet, the moment it was away — jerk! he was as erect, and carried his head as high, as ever.

To have taken the field openly against his rival would have been madness; for he was not a man to be thwarted in his amours, any more than that stormy lover Achilles.[1] Ichabod, therefore, made his advances in a quiet and gently insinuating manner. Under cover of his character of singing-master, he made frequent visits at the farmhouse; not that he had anything to apprehend from the meddlesome interference of parents, which is so often a stumbling-block in the path of lovers. Balt Van Tassel was an easy, indulgent soul. He loved his daughter better even than his pipe, and, like a reasonable man and an excellent father, let her have her way in everything. His notable little wife, too, had enough to do to attend to her housekeeping and manage the poultry; for, as she sagely observed, ducks and geese are foolish things, and must be looked after, but girls can take care of themselves. Thus, while the busy dame bustled about the house, or plied her spinning-wheel at one end of the piazza, honest Balt would sit smoking his evening pipe at the other, watching the achievements of a little wooden warrior, who, armed with a sword in each hand, was most valiantly fighting the wind on the pinnacle of the barn. In the mean time Ichabod would carry on his suit with the daughter by the side of the spring under the great elm, or sauntering along in the twilight, that hour so favorable to the lover's eloquence.

---

[1] A famous Greek warrior of Homer's Iliad. Achilles, in a dispute about his lady-love Briseis, becomes angered against Agamemnon, commander-in-chief of the allied Greeks besieging Troy or Ilion (hence the name "Iliad"), and refuses to fight. The Trojans prevail for a time. Patroclus, Achilles' friend, falls; and Achilles in wrath flies to battle, kills Hector (chief of the Trojans), and turns the tide of battle against them.

I profess not to know how women's hearts are wooed and won. To me they have always been matters of riddle and admiration. Some seem to have but one vulnerable point, or door of access; while others have a thousand avenues, and may be captured in a thousand different ways. It is a great triumph of skill to gain the former, but a still greater proof of generalship to maintain possession of the latter, for a man must battle for his fortress at every door and window. He who wins a thousand common hearts is therefore entitled to some renown; but he who keeps undisputed sway over the heart of a coquette is indeed a hero. Certain it is, this was not the case with the redoubtable Brom Bones; and, from the moment Ichabod Crane made his advances, the interests of the former evidently declined. His horse was no longer seen tied at the palings on Sunday nights, and a deadly feud gradually arose between him and the preceptor of Sleepy Hollow.

Brom, who had a degree of rough chivalry in his nature, would fain have carried matters to open warfare, and settled their pretensions to the lady according to the mode of those most concise and simple reasoners, the knights-errant of yore, by single combat; but Ichabod was too conscious of the superior might of his adversary to enter the lists against him. He had overheard the boast of Bones, that he would " double the schoolmaster up and put him on a shelf;" and he was too wary to give him an opportunity. There was something extremely provoking in this obstinately pacific system: it left Brom no alternative but to draw upon the funds of rustic waggery in his disposition, and to play off boorish practical jokes upon his rival. Ichabod became the object of whimsical persecution to Bones and his gang of rough riders. They harried his hitherto peaceful domains; smoked out his singing-school by stopping up the chimney; broke into the schoolhouse at night, in spite of its formidable fastenings of withe and window stakes, and turned everything topsy-turvy: so that the poor schoolmaster began to think all the witches in the country held their meetings there. But, what was still more annoying,

Brom took all opportunities of turning him into ridicule in presence of his mistress, and had a scoundrel dog whom he taught to whine in the most ludicrous manner, and introduced as a rival of Ichabod's to instruct her in psalmody.

In this way matters went on for some time, without producing any material effect on the relative situations of the contending powers. On a fine autumnal afternoon, Ichabod, in pensive mood, sat enthroned on the lofty stool from whence he usually watched all the concerns of his little literary realm. In his hand he swayed a ferule, that scepter of despotic power; the birch of justice reposed on three nails behind the throne, a constant terror to evil doers; while on the desk before him might be seen sundry contraband articles and prohibited weapons, detected upon the persons of idle urchins, such as half-munched apples, popguns, whirligigs, fly-cages, and whole legions of rampant little paper game-cocks. Apparently there had been some appalling act of justice recently inflicted; for his scholars were all busily intent upon their books, or slyly whispering behind them with one eye kept upon the master, and a kind of buzzing stillness reigned throughout the schoolroom. It was suddenly interrupted by the appearance of a negro, in tow-cloth jacket and trousers, a round-crowned fragment of a hat, like the cap of Mercury,[1] and mounted on the back of a ragged, wild, half-broken colt, which he managed with a rope by way of halter. He came clattering up to the school door with an invitation to Ichabod to attend a merry-making, or "quilting frolic," to be held that evening at Mynheer Van Tassel's; and having delivered his message with that air of importance, and effort at fine language, which a negro is apt to display on petty embassies of the kind, he dashed over the brook, and was seen scampering away up the hollow, full of the importance and hurry of his mission.

All was now bustle and hubbub in the late quiet schoolroom. The scholars were hurried through their lessons without stopping

[1] The Roman god who presided over barter, trade, and all commercial dealings.

at trifles. Those who were nimble skipped over half with impunity; and those who were tardy had a smart application now
and then in the rear, to quicken their speed, or help them over a
tall word. Books were flung aside without being put away on
the shelves; inkstands were overturned, benches thrown down;
and the whole school was turned loose an hour before the usual
time, bursting forth like a legion of young imps, yelping and
racketing about the green, in joy at their early emancipation.

The gallant Ichabod now spent at least an extra half hour at
his toilet, brushing and furbishing up his best and indeed only suit
of rusty black, and arranging his looks by a bit of broken look-
ing-glass that hung up in the schoolhouse. That he might make
his appearance before his mistress in the true style of a cavalier,
he borrowed a horse from the farmer with whom he was domi-
ciliated, a choleric old Dutchman of the name of Hans Van Ripper, and, thus gallantly mounted, issued forth, like a knight-errant
in quest of adventures. But it is meet I should, in the true spirit
of romantic story, give some account of the looks and equipments
of my hero and his steed. The animal he bestrode was a broken-
down plow-horse, that had outlived almost everything but his
viciousness. He was gaunt and shagged, with a ewe neck, and
a head like a hammer. His rusty mane and tail were tangled
and knotted with burrs. One eye had lost its pupil, and was
glaring and spectral, but the other had the gleam of a genuine
devil in it. Still he must have had fire and mettle in his day, if
we may judge from his name, which was Gunpowder. He had,
in fact, been a favorite steed of his master's, the choleric Van
Ripper, who was a furious rider, and had infused, very probably,
some of his own spirit into the animal; for, old and broken-down
as he looked, there was more of the lurking devil in him than in
any young filly in the country.

Ichabod was a suitable figure for such a steed. He rode with
short stirrups, which brought his knees nearly up to the pommel
of the saddle; his sharp elbows stuck out like grasshoppers'; he
carried his whip perpendicularly in his hand, like a scepter; and,

as the horse jogged on, the motion of his arms was not unlike the flapping of a pair of wings. A small wool hat rested on the top of his nose, for so his scanty strip of forehead might be called; and the skirts of his black coat fluttered out almost to the horse's tail. Such was the appearance of Ichabod and his steed, as they shambled out of the gate of Hans Van Ripper; and it was altogether such an apparition as is seldom to be met with in broad daylight.

It was, as I have said, a fine autumnal day. The sky was clear and serene, and nature wore that rich and golden livery which we always associate with the idea of abundance. The forests had put on their sober brown and yellow, while some trees of the tenderer kind had been nipped by the frost into brilliant dyes of orange, purple, and scarlet. Streaming files of wild ducks began to make their appearance high in the air. The bark of the squirrel might be heard from the groves of beech and hickory nuts, and the pensive whistle of the quail at intervals from the neighboring stubble-field.

The small birds were taking their farewell banquets. In the fullness of their revelry, they fluttered, chirping and frolicking, from bush to bush, and tree to tree, capricious from the very profusion and variety around them. There was the honest cock-robin, the favorite game of stripling sportsmen, with its loud, querulous note; and the twittering blackbirds flying in sable clouds; and the golden-winged woodpecker, with his crimson crest, his broad, black gorget, and splendid plumage; and the cedar bird, with its red-tipped wings and yellow-tipped tail, and its little monteiro cap[1] of feathers; and the blue jay, that noisy coxcomb, in his gay, light-blue coat and white underclothes, screaming and chattering, nodding and bobbing and bowing, and pretending to be on good terms with every songster of the grove.

[1] Montero cap (Spanish, *montera*), a kind of cap, originally a hunting-cap; from *montero* ("a huntsman"). It has a spherical crown, and a flap round it that may be drawn down over the ears.

As Ichabod jogged slowly on his way, his eye, ever open to every symptom of culinary abundance, ranged with delight over the treasures of jolly autumn. On all sides he beheld vast store of apples,— some hanging in oppressive opulence on the trees, some gathered into baskets and barrels for the market, others heaped up in rich piles for the cider-press. Farther on he beheld great fields of Indian corn, with its golden ears peeping from their leafy coverts, and holding out the promise of cakes and hasty pudding; and the yellow pumpkins lying beneath them, turning up their fair, round bellies to the sun, and giving ample prospects of the most luxurious of pies; and anon he passed the fragrant buckwheat fields, breathing the odor of the beehive; and as he beheld them, soft anticipations stole over his mind of dainty slapjacks, well buttered, and garnished with honey or treacle, by the delicate little dimpled hand of Katrina Van Tassel.

Thus feeding his mind with many sweet thoughts and "sugared suppositions," he journeyed along the sides of a range of hills which look out upon some of the goodliest scenes of the mighty Hudson. The sun gradually wheeled his broad disk down into the west. The wide bosom of the Tappan Zee lay motionless and glassy, excepting that here and there a gentle undulation waved, and prolonged the blue shadow of the distant mountain. A few amber clouds floated in the sky, without a breath of air to move them. The horizon was of a fine, golden tint, changing gradually into a pure apple-green, and from that into the deep-blue of the mid-heaven. A slanting ray lingered on the woody crests of the precipices that overhung some parts of the river, giving greater depth to the dark gray and purple of their rocky sides. A sloop was loitering in the distance, dropping slowly down with the tide, her sail hanging uselessly against the mast; and, as the reflection of the sky gleamed along the still water, it seemed as if the vessel was suspended in the air.

It was toward evening that Ichabod arrived at the castle of the Herr Van Tassel, which he found thronged with the pride and flower of the adjacent country,—old farmers, a spare, leathern-faced race, in homespun coats and breeches, blue stockings, huge shoes, and magnificent pewter buckles; their brisk, withered little dames, in close crimped caps, long-waisted gowns, homespun petticoats, with scissors and pincushions, and gay calico pockets hanging on the outside; buxom lasses, almost as antiquated as their mothers, excepting where a straw hat, a fine ribbon, or perhaps a white frock, gave symptoms of city innovations; the sons, in short, square-skirted coats with rows of stupendous brass buttons, and their hair generally queued in the fashion of the times, especially if they could procure an eel-skin for the purpose, it being esteemed throughout the country as a potent nourisher and strengthener of the hair.

Brom Bones, however, was the hero of the scene, having come to the gathering on his favorite steed Daredevil,—a creature, like himself, full of mettle and mischief, and which no one but himself could manage. He was, in fact, noted for preferring vicious animals, given to all kinds of tricks, which kept the rider in constant risk of his neck; for he held a tractable, well-broken horse as unworthy of a lad of spirit.

Fain would I pause to dwell upon the world of charms that burst upon the enraptured gaze of my hero, as he entered the state parlor of Van Tassel's mansion; not those of the bevy of buxom lasses, with their luxurious display of red and white, but the ample charms of a genuine Dutch country tea-table, in the sumptuous time of autumn. Such heaped-up platters of cakes of various and almost indescribable kinds, known only to experienced Dutch housewives! There was the doughty doughnut, the tender oly-koek,[1] and the crisp and crumbling cruller; sweet cakes and short cakes, ginger cakes and honey cakes, and the whole family of cakes; and then there were apple pies and peach pies and pumpkin pies; besides slices of ham and smoked beef; and, moreover, delectable dishes of preserved plums, and

---

[1] A kind of Dutch cake, made of dough sweetened, and fried in lard.

peaches, and pears, and quinces; not to mention broiled shad and roasted chickens; together with bowls of milk and cream; all mingled higgledy-piggledy, pretty much as I have enumerated them, with the motherly teapot sending up its clouds of vapor from the midst — Heaven bless the mark! I want breath and time to discuss this banquet as it deserves, and am too eager to get on with my story. Happily, Ichabod Crane was not in so great a hurry as his historian, but did ample justice to every dainty.

He was a kind and thankful creature, whose heart dilated in proportion as his skin was filled with good cheer, and whose spirits rose with eating as some men's do with drink. He could not help, too, rolling his large eyes round him as he ate, and chuckling with the possibility that he might one day be lord of all this scene of almost unimaginable luxury and splendor. Then, he thought, how soon he'd turn his back upon the old school-house; snap his fingers in the face of Hans Van Ripper, and every other niggardly patron; and kick any itinerant pedagogue out of doors that should dare to call him comrade!

Old Baltus Van Tassel moved about among his guests with a face dilated with content and good humor, round and jolly as the harvest moon. His hospitable attentions were brief but expressive, being confined to a shake of the hand, a slap on the shoulder, a loud laugh, and a pressing invitation to "fall to, and help themselves."

And now the sound of the music from the common room, or hall, summoned to the dance. The musician was an old gray-headed negro, who had been the itinerant orchestra of the neighborhood for more than half a century. His instrument was as old and battered as himself. The greater part of the time he scraped away on two or three strings, accompanying every movement of the bow with a motion of the head, bowing almost to the ground, and stamping with his foot whenever a fresh couple were to start.

Ichabod prided himself upon his dancing as much as upon his

vocal powers. Not a limb, not a fiber about him, was idle; and
to have seen his loosely hung frame in full motion, and clattering
about the room, you would have thought St. Vitus[1] himself, that
blessed patron of the dance, was figuring before you in person.
He was the admiration of all the negroes, who, having gathered,
of all ages and sizes, from the farm and the neighborhood, stood
forming a pyramid of shining black faces at every door and window, gazing with delight at the scene, rolling their white eyeballs,
and showing grinning rows of ivory from ear to ear.   How could
the flogger of urchins be otherwise than animated and joyous?
The lady of his heart was his partner in the dance, and smiling
graciously in reply to all his amorous oglings; while Brom Bones,
sorely smitten with love and jealousy, sat brooding by himself in
one corner.

When the dance was at an end, Ichabod was attracted to a
knot of the sager folks, who, with old Van Tassel, sat smoking
at one end of the piazza, gossiping over former times, and
drawling out long stories about the war.

This neighborhood, at the time of which I am speaking, was
one of those highly favored places which abound with chronicle
and great men.   The British and American line had run near
it during the war: it had therefore been the scene of marauding,
and infested with refugees, cowboys, and all kinds of border
chivalry.   Just sufficient time had elapsed to enable each story-
teller to dress up his tale with a little becoming fiction, and, in
the indistinctness of his recollection, to make himself the hero of
every exploit.

There was the story of Doffue Martling, a large, blue-bearded
Dutchman, who had nearly taken a British frigate with an old
iron nine-pounder from a mud breastwork, only that his gun burst
at the sixth discharge.   And there was an old gentleman who

---

[1] The patron saint of dancers and actors, and invoked against the disease
known as "St. Vitus's dance."   He is the patron of Saxony, Bohemia, and
Sicily, and throughout Germany ranks as one of the fourteen "Nothelfer"
of the Church.

shall be nameless, being too rich a mynheer[1] to be lightly mentioned, who in the battle of Whiteplains,[2] being an excellent master of defense, parried a musket-ball with a small sword, insomuch that he absolutely felt it whiz round the blade, and glance off at the hilt, in proof of which he was ready at any time to show the sword, with the hilt a little bent. There were several more that had been equally great in the field, not one of whom but was persuaded that he had a considerable hand in bringing the war to a happy termination.

But all these were nothing to the tales of ghosts and apparitions that succeeded. The neighborhood is rich in legendary treasures of the kind. Local tales and superstitions thrive best in these sheltered, long-settled retreats, but are trampled under foot by the shifting throng that forms the population of most of our country places. Besides, there is no encouragement for ghosts in most of our villages, for they have scarcely had time to finish their first nap, and turn themselves in their graves, before their surviving friends have traveled away from the neighborhood ; so that, when they turn out at night to walk their rounds, they have no acquaintance left to call upon. This is, perhaps, the reason why we so seldom hear of ghosts, except in our long-established Dutch communities.

The immediate cause, however, of the prevalence of supernatural stories in these parts, was doubtless owing to the vicinity of Sleepy Hollow. There was a contagion in the very air that blew from that haunted region : it breathed forth an atmosphere of dreams and fancies infecting all the land. Several of the Sleepy Hollow people were present at Van Tassel's, and, as usual, were doling out their wild and wonderful legends. Many dismal tales

---

1 From the Dutch *mijn heer*, equivalent to the German *mein Herr* (" my master," " my lord "), our " sir " or " Mr.," a term of respectful address employed by the Dutch ; hence also a Dutchman.

2 At Whiteplains, twenty-five miles northeast of New York, the Americans were driven back by the British under Gen. Howe, and compelled to withdraw to New Jersey, October, 1776.

were told about funeral trains, and mourning cries and wailings, heard and seen about the great tree where the unfortunate Major André[1] was taken, and which stood in the neighborhood. Some mention was made also of the woman in white that haunted the dark glen at Raven Rock, and was often heard to shriek on winter nights before a storm, having perished there in the snow. The chief part of the stories, however, turned upon the favorite specter of Sleepy Hollow, the headless horseman, who had been heard several times of late, patrolling the country, and, it was said, tethered his horse nightly among the graves in the churchyard.

The sequestered situation of this church seems always to have made it a favorite haunt of troubled spirits. It stands on a knoll, surrounded by locust-trees and lofty elms, from among which its decent, whitewashed walls shine modestly forth, like Christian purity beaming through the shades of retirement. A gentle slope descends from it to a silver sheet of water, bordered by high trees, between which peeps may be caught at the blue hills of the Hudson. To look upon its grass-grown yard, where the sunbeams seem to sleep so quietly, one would think that there, at least, the dead might rest in peace. On one side of the church extends a wide, woody dell, along which raves a large brook among broken rocks and trunks of fallen trees. Over a deep black part of the stream, not far from the church, was formerly thrown a wooden bridge. The road that led to it, and the bridge itself, were thickly shaded by overhanging trees, which cast a gloom about it, even in the daytime, but occasioned a fearful

[1] John André was born in London in 1751. He became an adjutant-general in the British army of the American Revolution. Benedict Arnold, who commanded the American fortress of West Point, made arrangements to betray that place into the hands of the British general Sir Henry Clinton. André was associated with Arnold in this plot, which was frustrated and defeated by the capture of André, who had been sent by Arnold with letters. André was tried by a court-martial, and condemned to be hanged as a spy. He was executed at Tappantown, Oct. 2, 1780. In 1821 his remains were transferred to England, and interred in Westminster Abbey.

darkness at night. Such was one of the favorite haunts of the headless horseman, and the place where he was most frequently encountered. The tale was told of old Brouwer, a most heretical disbeliever in ghosts, — how he met the horseman returning from his foray into Sleepy Hollow, and was obliged to get up behind him; how they galloped over bush and brake, over hill and swamp, until they reached the bridge, when the horseman suddenly turned into a skeleton, threw old Brouwer into the brook, and sprang away over the tree-tops with a clap of thunder.

This story was immediately matched by a thrice marvelous adventure of Brom Bones, who made light of the Galloping Hessian as an arrant jockey. He affirmed, that, on returning one night from the neighboring village of Sing Sing, he had been overtaken by this midnight trooper; that he had offered to race with him for a bowl of punch, and should have won it, too (for Daredevil beat the goblin horse all hollow), but, just as they came to the church bridge, the Hessian bolted, and vanished in a flash of fire.

All these tales told in that drowsy undertone with which men talk in the dark, the countenances of the listeners only now and then receiving a casual gleam from the glare of a pipe, sank deep in the mind of Ichabod. He repaid them in kind with large extracts from his invaluable author Cotton Mather, and added many marvelous events that had taken place in his native State of Connecticut, and fearful sights which he had seen in his nightly walks about Sleepy Hollow.

The revel now gradually broke up. The old farmers gathered together their families in their wagons, and were heard for some time rattling along the hollow roads, and over the distant hills. Some of the damsels mounted on pillions[1] behind their favorite swains; and their light-hearted laughter, mingling with the clatter of hoofs, echoed along the silent woodlands, sounding fainter and fainter until they gradually died away, and the late scene of

[1] A cushion adjusted to a saddle at the back, serving as a kind of seat for another person riding behind.

noise and frolic was all silent and deserted. Ichabod only lingered behind, according to the custom of country lovers, to have
a *tête-à-tête* with the heiress, fully convinced that he was now on
the high road to success. What passed at this interview I will
not pretend to say, for in fact I do not know. Something, however, I fear me, must have gone wrong; for he certainly sallied
forth, after no very great interval, with an air quite desolate and
chopfallen. Oh these women, these women! Could that girl
have been playing off any of her coquettish tricks? Was her
encouragement of the poor pedagogue all a mere sham to secure
her conquest of his rival? Heaven only knows, not I! Let it
suffice to say, Ichabod stole forth with the air of one who had
been sacking a hen-roost rather than a fair lady's heart. Without looking to the right or left to notice the scene of rural wealth
on which he had so often gloated, he went straight to the stable,
and, with several hearty cuffs and kicks, roused his steed most
uncourteously from the comfortable quarters in which he was
soundly sleeping, dreaming of mountains of corn and oats, and
whole valleys of timothy and clover.

It was the very witching time of night, that Ichabod, heavy-
hearted and crestfallen, pursued his travel homewards along the
sides of the lofty hills which rise above Tarrytown, and which
he had traversed so cheerily in the afternoon. The hour was as
dismal as himself. Far below him the Tappan Zee spread its
dusky and indistinct waste of waters, with here and there the tall
mast of a sloop riding quietly at anchor under the land. In the
dead hush of midnight he could even hear the barking of the
watch-dog from the opposite shore of the Hudson, but it was so
vague and faint as only to give an idea of his distance from this
faithful companion of man. Now and then, too, the long-drawn
crowing of a cock, accidentally awakened, would sound far, far
off, from some farmhouse away among the hills; but it was like
a dreaming sound in his ear. No signs of life occurred near
him, but occasionally the melancholy chirp of a cricket, or
perhaps the guttural twang of a bull-frog from a neighboring

marsh, as if sleeping uncomfortably, and turning suddenly in his bed.

All the stories of ghosts and goblins that he had heard in the afternoon, now came crowding upon his recollection. The night grew darker and darker. The stars seemed to sink deeper in the sky, and driving clouds occasionally hid them from his sight. He had never felt so lonely and dismal. He was, moreover, approaching the very place where many of the scenes of the ghost stories had been laid. In the center of the road stood an enormous tulip-tree, which towered like a giant above all the other trees of the neighborhood, and formed a kind of landmark. Its limbs were gnarled and fantastic, large enough to form trunks for ordinary trees, twisting down almost to the earth, and rising again into the air. It was connected with the tragical story of the unfortunate André who had been taken prisoner hard by, and was universally known by the name of Major André's tree. The common people regarded it with a mixture of respect and superstition, partly out of sympathy for the fate of its ill-starred namesake, and partly from the tales of strange sights and doleful lamentations told concerning it.

As Ichabod approached this fearful tree, he began to whistle. He thought his whistle was answered: it was but a blast sweeping sharply through the dry branches. As he approached a little nearer, he thought he saw something white hanging in the midst of the tree. He paused, and ceased whistling, but, on looking more narrowly, perceived that it was a place where the tree had been scathed by lightning, and the white wood laid bare. Suddenly he heard a groan. His teeth chattered, and his knees smote against the saddle. It was but the rubbing of one huge bough upon another, as they were swayed about by the breeze. He passed the tree in safety, but new perils lay before him.

About two hundred yards from the tree a small brook crossed the road, and ran into a marshy and thickly wooded glen, known by the name of Wiley's Swamp. A few rough logs laid side by side served for a bridge over this stream. On that side of the road where the brook entered the wood, a group of oaks and chestnuts, matted thick with wild grape-vines, threw a cavernous gloom over it. To pass this bridge was the severest trial. It was at this identical spot that the unfortunate André was captured, and under the covert of those chestnuts and vines were the sturdy yeomen concealed who surprised him. This has ever since been considered a haunted stream, and fearful are the feelings of the schoolboy who has to pass it alone after dark.

As he approached the stream his heart began to thump. He summoned up, however, all his resolution, gave his horse half a score of kicks in the ribs, and attempted to dash briskly across the bridge; but, instead of starting forward, the perverse old animal made a lateral movement, and ran broadside against the fence. Ichabod, whose fears increased with the delay, jerked the reins on the other side, and kicked lustily with the contrary foot. It was all in vain. His steed started, it is true, but it was only to plunge to the opposite side of the road into a thicket of brambles and alder bushes. The schoolmaster now bestowed both whip and heel upon the starveling ribs of old Gunpowder, who dashed forward, snuffling and snorting, but came to a stand just by the bridge with a suddenness that had nearly sent his rider sprawling over his head. Just at this moment a plashy tramp by the side of the bridge caught the sensitive ear of Ichabod. In the dark shadow of the grove, on the margin of the brook, he beheld something huge, misshapen, black, and towering. It stirred not, but seemed gathered up in the gloom, like some gigantic monster ready to spring upon the traveler.

The hair of the affrighted pedagogue rose upon his head with terror. What was to be done? To turn and fly was now too late; and, besides, what chance was there of escaping ghost or goblin, if such it was, which could ride upon the wings of the wind? Summoning up, therefore, a show of courage, he demanded in stammering accents, "Who are you?" He received no reply. He repeated his demand in a still more agitated voice. Still there was no answer. Once more he cudgeled the sides of the inflexible Gunpowder, and, shutting his eyes, broke forth with involuntary fervor into a psalm tune. Just then the shadowy object of alarm put itself in motion, and, with a scramble and a bound, stood at once in the middle of the road. Though the night was dark and dismal, yet the form of the unknown might now in some degree be ascertained. He appeared to be a horseman of large dimensions, and mounted on a black horse of powerful frame. He made no offer of molestation or sociability, but kept aloof on one side of the road, jogging along on the blind side of old Gunpowder, who had now got over his fright and waywardness.

Ichabod, who had no relish for this strange midnight companion, and bethought himself of the adventure of Brom Bones with the Galloping Hessian, now quickened his steed, in hopes of leaving him behind. The stranger, however, quickened his horse to an equal pace. Ichabod pulled up, and fell into a walk, thinking to lag behind: the other did the same. His heart began to sink within him. He endeavored to resume his psalm tune; but his parched tongue clove to the roof of his mouth, and he could not utter a stave. There was something in the moody and dogged silence of this pertinacious companion that was mysterious and appalling. It was soon fearfully accounted for. On mounting a rising ground, which brought the figure of his fellow-traveler in relief against the sky, gigantic in height, and muffled in a cloak, Ichabod was horror-struck on perceiving that he was headless; but his horror was still more increased on observing that the head, which should have rested on his shoulders, was carried before him on the pommel of his saddle. His terror rose to desperation. He reined a shower of kicks and blows upon Gunpowder, hoping, by a sudden movement, to give his companion the slip; but the specter started full jump with him. Away then they dashed, through thick and thin; stones flying, and sparks flashing, at every bound. Ichabod's flimsy garments fluttered in the air, as he stretched his long, lank body away over his horse's head, in the eagerness of his flight.

They had now reached the road which turns off to Sleepy Hollow; but Gunpowder, who seemed possessed with a demon, instead of keeping up it, made an opposite turn, and plunged headlong downhill to the left. This road leads through a sandy hollow, shaded by trees for about a quarter of a mile, where it crosses the bridge famous in goblin story; and just beyond swells the green knoll on which stands the whitewashed church.

As yet the panic of the steed had given his unskillful rider an apparent advantage in the chase; but, just as he had got halfway through the hollow, the girths of the saddle gave way, and he felt it slipping from under him. He seized it by the pommel, and endeavored to hold it firm, but in vain; and had just time to save himself by clasping old Gunpowder round the neck, when the saddle fell to the earth, and he heard it trampled under foot by his pursuer. For a moment the terror of Hans Van Ripper's wrath passed across his mind, for it was his Sunday saddle; but this was no time for petty fears. The goblin was hard on his haunches; and (unskillful rider that he was) he had much ado to maintain his seat, sometimes slipping on one side, sometimes on another, and sometimes jolted on the high ridge of his horse's backbone with a violence that he verily feared would cleave him asunder.

An opening in the trees now cheered him with the hopes that the church bridge was at hand. The wavering reflection of a silver star in the bosom of the brook told him that he was not mistaken. He saw the walls of the church dimly glaring under the trees beyond. He recollected the place where Brom Bones's ghostly competitor had disappeared. " If I can but reach that bridge," thought Ichabod, " I am safe." Just then he heard the black steed panting and blowing close behind him. He even fancied that he felt his hot breath. Another convulsive kick in the ribs, and old Gunpowder sprang upon the bridge; he thundered over the resounding planks; he gained the opposite side; and now Ichabod cast a look behind to see if his pursuer should vanish, according to rule, in a flash of fire and brimstone. Just then he saw the goblin rising in his stirrups, and in the very act of hurling his head at him. Ichabod endeavored to dodge the horrible missile, but too late. It encountered his cranium with a tremendous crash. He was tumbled headlong into the dust; and Gunpowder, the black steed, and the goblin rider, passed by like a whirlwind.

The next morning the old horse was found without his saddle, and with the bridle under his feet, soberly cropping the grass at his master's gate. Ichabod did not make his appearance at breakfast. Dinner-hour came, but no Ichabod. The boys assembled at the schoolhouse, and strolled idly about the banks of the brook; but no schoolmaster. Hans Van Ripper now began to feel some uneasiness about the fate of poor Ichabod and his saddle. An inquiry was set on foot, and after diligent investigation they came upon his traces. In one part of the road leading to the church was found the saddle trampled in the dirt. The tracks of horses' hoofs deeply dented in the road, and evidently at furious speed, were traced to the bridge, beyond which, on the bank of a broad part of the brook, where the water ran deep and black, was found the hat of the unfortunate Ichabod, and close beside it a shattered pumpkin.

The brook was searched, but the body of the schoolmaster was not to be discovered. Hans Van Ripper, as executor of his estate, examined the bundle which contained all his worldly effects. They consisted of two shirts and a half; two stocks for the neck : a pair or two of worsted stockings; an old pair of corduroy small-clothes; a rusty razor; a book of psalm tunes, full of dogs' ears; and a broken pitchpipe. As to the books and furniture of the schoolhouse, they belonged to the community, excepting Cotton Mather's "History of Witchcraft," a "New England Almanac," and a book of dreams and fortune-telling; in which last was a sheet of foolscap much scribbled and blotted by several fruitless attempts to make a copy of verses in honor of the heiress of Van Tassel. These magic books and the poetic scrawl were forthwith consigned to the flames by Hans Van Ripper.

wno from that time forward determined to send his children no
more to school, observing that he never knew any good come of
this same reading and writing. Whatever money the schoolmaster possessed, and he had received his quarter's pay but a
day or two before, he must have had about his person at the
time of his disappearance.

The mysterious event caused much speculation at the church
on the following Sunday. Knots of gazers and gossips were
collected in the churchyard, at the bridge, and at the spot where
the hat and pumpkin had been found. The stories of Brouwer,
of Bones, and a whole budget of others, were called to mind;
and when they had diligently considered them all, and compared
them with the symptoms of the present case, they shook their
heads, and came to the conclusion that Ichabod had been carried off by the Galloping Hessian. As he was a bachelor, and
in nobody's debt, nobody troubled his head any more about him.
The school was removed to a different quarter of the hollow, and
another pedagogue reigned in his stead.

It is true, an old farmer, who had been down to New York on
a visit several years after, and from whom this account of the
ghostly adventure was received, brought home the intelligence
that Ichabod Crane was still alive; that he had left the neighborhood, partly through fear of the goblin and Hans Van Ripper, and partly in mortification at having been suddenly dismissed
by the heiress; that he had changed his quarters to a distant
part of the country, had kept school and studied law at the same
time, had been admitted to the bar, turned politician, election-
eered, written for the newspapers, and finally had been made a
justice of the Ten Pound Court. Brom Bones, too, who shortly
after his rival's disappearance conducted the blooming Katrina
in triumph to the altar, was observed to look exceedingly knowing whenever the story of Ichabod was related, and always burst
into a hearty laugh at the mention of the pumpkin, which led
some to suspect that he knew more about the matter than he
chose to tell.

The old country wives, however, who are the best judges of these matters, maintain to this day that Ichabod was spirited away by supernatural means; and it is a favorite story often told about the neighborhood round the winter evening fire. The bridge became more than ever an object of superstitious awe; and that may be the reason why the road has been altered of late years, so as to approach the church by the border of the millpond. The schoolhouse, being deserted, soon fell to decay, and was reported to be haunted by the ghost of the unfortunate pedagogue; and the plow-boy, loitering homeward of a still summer evening, has often fancied his voice at a distance, chanting a melancholy psalm tune among the tranquil solitudes of Sleepy Hollow.

POSTSCRIPT.

[*Found in the handwriting of Mr. Knickerbocker.*]

THE preceding tale is given almost in the precise words in which I heard it related at a corporation meeting of the ancient city of the Manhattoes,[1] at which were present many of its sagest and most illustrious burghers. The narrator was a pleasant, shabby, gentlemanly old fellow, in pepper-and-salt clothes, with a sadly humorous face; and one whom I strongly suspected of being poor, he made such efforts to be entertaining. When his story was concluded, there was much laughter and approbation, particularly from two or three deputy aldermen, who had been asleep the greater part of the time. There was, however, one tall, dry-looking old gentleman, with beetling eyebrows, who maintained a grave and rather severe face throughout; now and then folding his arms, inclining his head, and looking down upon the floor, as if turning a doubt over in his mind. He was one of your wary men, who never laugh but upon good grounds, when they have reason and the law on their side. When the mirth of the rest of the company had subsided and silence was restored, he leaned one arm on the elbow of his chair, and, sticking the other akimbo, demanded, with a slight but exceedingly sage motion of the head and contraction of the brow, what was the moral of the story, and what it went to prove.

The story-teller, who was just putting a glass of wine to his lips, as a refreshment after his toils, paused for a moment, looked at his inquirer with an

---

[1] Manhattan, i.e., New York.

air of infinite deference, and, lowering the glass slowly to the table, observed that the story was intended most logically to prove, —

"That there is no situation in life but has its advantages and pleasures, provided we will but take a joke as we find it.

"That therefore he that runs races with goblin troopers is likely to have rough riding of it.

"Ergo, for a country schoolmaster to be refused the hand of a Dutch heiress, is a certain step to high preferment in the State."

The cautious old gentleman knit his brows tenfold closer after this explanation, being sorely puzzled by the ratiocination of the syllogism; while, methought, the one in pepper-and-salt eyed him with something of a triumphant leer. At length he observed that all this was very well, but still he thought the story a little on the extravagant: there were one or two points on which he had his doubts.

"Faith, sir," replied the story-teller, "as to that matter, I don't believe one half of it myself."

D. K.

RIP VAN WINKLE.

[*A Posthumous Writing of Diedrich Knickerbocker.*]

"By Woden, God of Saxons,
From whence comes Wensday, that is Wodensday,
Truth is a thing that ever I will keep
Unto thylke day in which I creep into
My supulchre."

CARTWRIGHT.

WHOEVER has made a voyage up the Hudson must remember the Catskill Mountains. They are a dismembered branch of the great Appalachian family, and are seen away to the west of the river, swelling up to a noble height, and lording it over the surrounding country. Every change of season, every change of weather, indeed every hour of the day, produces some change in the magical hues and shapes of these mountains; and they are regarded by all the good wives, far and near, as perfect barometers. When the weather is fair and settled, they are clothed in blue and purple, and print their bold outlines on the

clear evening sky; but sometimes, when the rest of the landscape is cloudless, they will gather a hood of gray vapors about
their summits, which, in the last rays of the setting sun, will glow
and light up like a crown of glory.

At the foot of these fairy mountains the voyager may have
descried the light smoke curling up from a village, whose shingle-
roofs gleam among the trees, just where the blue tints of the up-
land melt away into the fresh green of the nearer landscape.   It
is a little village, of great antiquity, having been founded by some
of the Dutch colonists in the early times of the province, just
about the beginning of the government of the good Peter Stuyvesant;[1] (may he rest in peace!) and there were some of the
houses of the original settlers standing within a few years, built
of small, yellow bricks brought from Holland, having latticed
windows and gable fronts, surmounted with weathercocks.

In that same village, and in one of these very houses (which,
to tell the precise truth, was sadly time-worn and weather-beaten),
there lived many years since, while the country was yet a province of Great Britain, a simple, good-natured fellow of the name
of Rip Van Winkle.   He was a descendant of the Van Winkles
who figured so gallantly in the chivalrous days of Peter Stuyvesant, and accompanied him to the siege of Fort Christina.[2]   He
inherited, however, but little of the martial character of his ancestors.   I have observed that he was a simple, good-natured
man; he was, moreover, a kind neighbor, and an obedient, hen-
pecked husband.   Indeed, to the latter circumstance might be
owing that meekness of spirit which gained him such universal
popularity; for those men are most apt to be obsequious and
conciliating abroad, who are under the discipline of shrews at
home.   Their tempers, doubtless, are rendered pliant and malle-
able in the fiery furnace of domestic tribulation; and a curtain

---

[1] Governor of Manhattan Island in 1647.

[2] Fort Christina, or Christiana, was a Swedish fort, situated five miles
north of Fort Cassimir (now Newcastle, Del.), attacked and captured by the
Dutch of New Netherlands in 1655.

lecture is worth all the sermons in the world for teaching the virtues of patience and long-suffering. A termagant wife may therefore, in some respects, be considered a tolerable blessing; and, if so, Rip Van Winkle was thrice blessed.

Certain it is, that he was a great favorite among all the good wives of the village, who, as usual with the amiable sex, took his part in all family squabbles, and never failed, whenever they talked those matters over in their evening gossipings, to lay all the blame on Dame Van Winkle. The children of the village, too, would shout with joy whenever he approached. He assisted at their sports, made their playthings, taught them to fly kites and shoot marbles, and told them long stories of ghosts, witches, and Indians. Whenever he went dodging about the village, he was surrounded by a troop of them, hanging on his skirts, clambering on his back, and playing a thousand tricks on him with impunity; and not a dog would bark at him throughout the neighborhood.

The great error in Rip's composition was an insuperable aversion to all kinds of profitable labor. It could not be from the want of assiduity or perseverance; for he would sit on a wet rock, with a rod as long and heavy as a Tartar's[1] lance, and fish all day without a murmur, even though he should not be encouraged by a single nibble. He would carry a fowling-piece on his shoulder for hours together, trudging through woods and swamps, and up hill and down dale, to shoot a few squirrels or wild pigeons. He would never refuse to assist a neighbor even in the roughest toil, and was a foremost man at all country frolics for husking Indian corn or building stone fences. The women of the village, too, used to employ him to run their errands, and to do such little odd jobs as their less obliging husbands would not do for them. In a word, Rip was ready to attend to anybody's business but his own; but as to doing family duty, and keeping his farm in order, he found it impossible.

In fact, he declared it was of no use to work on his farm. It

---

[1] See note, p. 108.

was the most pestilent little piece of ground in the whole country. Everything about it went wrong, and would go wrong, in spite of him. His fences were continually falling to pieces; his cow would either go astray, or get among the cabbages; weeds were sure to grow quicker in his fields than anywhere else; the rain always made a point of setting in just as he had some outdoor work to do: so that, though his patrimonial estate had dwindled away under his management acre by acre, until there was little more left than a mere patch of Indian corn and potatoes, yet it was the worst-conditioned farm in the neighborhood.

His children, too, were as ragged and wild as if they belonged to nobody. His son Rip, an urchin begotten in his own likeness, promised to inherit the habits with the old clothes of his father. He was generally seen trooping like a colt at his mother's heels, equipped in a pair of his father's cast-off galligaskins,[1] which he had much ado to hold up with one hand, as a fine lady does her train in bad weather.

Rip Van Winkle, however, was one of those happy mortals, of foolish, well-oiled dispositions, who take the world easy, eat white bread or brown, whichever can be got with least thought or trouble, and would rather starve on a penny than work for a pound. If left to himself, he would have whistled life away in perfect contentment; but his wife kept continually dinning in his ears about his idleness, his carelessness, and the ruin he was bringing on his family.

Morning, noon, and night, her tongue was incessantly going, and everything he said or did was sure to produce a torrent of household eloquence. Rip had but one way of replying to all lectures of the kind, and that, by frequent use, had grown into a habit. He shrugged his shoulders, shook his head, cast up his eyes, but said nothing. This, however, always provoked a fresh volley from his wife; so that he was fain to draw off his forces, and take to the outside of the house, — the only side which, in truth, belongs to a hen-pecked husband.

[1] A kind of wide breeches.

Rip's sole domestic adherent was his dog Wolf, who was as much hen-pecked as his master; for Dame Van Winkle regarded them as companions in idleness, and even looked upon Wolf with an evil eye, as the cause of his master's going so often astray. True it is, in all points of spirit befitting an honorable dog, he was as courageous an animal as ever scoured the woods; but what courage can withstand the ever-during and all-besetting terrors of a woman's tongue? The moment Wolf entered the house, his crest fell; his tail drooped to the ground or curled between his legs; he sneaked about with a gallows air, casting many a sidelong glance at Dame Van Winkle; and, at the least flourish of a broomstick or ladle, he would fly to the door with yelping precipitation.

Times grew worse and worse with Rip Van Winkle as years of matrimony rolled on. A tart temper never mellows with age, and a sharp tongue is the only edged tool that grows keener with constant use. For a long while he used to console himself, when driven from home, by frequenting a kind of perpetual club of the sages, philosophers, and other idle personages of the village, which held its sessions on a bench before a small inn, designated by a rubicund portrait of his Majesty George III.[1] Here they used to sit in the shade of a long, lazy, summer's day, talking listlessly over village gossip, or telling endless sleepy stories about nothing. But it would have been worth any statesman's money to have heard the profound discussions which sometimes took place, when by chance an old newspaper fell into their hands from some passing traveler. How solemnly they would listen to the contents, as drawled out by Derrick Van Bummel, the school-master, — a dapper, learned little man, who was not to be daunted by the most gigantic word in the dictionary! and how sagely they would deliberate upon public events some months after they had taken place!

The opinions of this junto were completely controlled by

---

[1] George III. (1738–1820) ascended the English throne in 1760, and reigned sixty years.

Nicholas Vedder, a patriarch of the village, and landlord of the inn, at the door of which he took his seat from morning till night, just moving sufficiently to avoid the sun, and keep in the shade of a large tree; so that the neighbors could tell the hour by his movements as accurately as by a sun-dial. It is true, he was rarely heard to speak, but smoked his pipe incessantly. His adherents, however (for every great man has his adherents), perfectly understood him, and knew how to gather his opinions. When anything that was read or related displeased him, he was observed to smoke his pipe vehemently, and to send forth short, frequent, and angry puffs; but, when pleased, he would inhale the smoke slowly and tranquilly, and emit it in light and placid clouds, and sometimes, taking the pipe from his mouth, and letting the fragrant vapor curl about his nose, would gravely nod his head in token of perfect approbation.

From even this stronghold the unlucky Rip was at length routed by his termagant wife, who would suddenly break in upon the tranquillity of the assemblage, and call the members all to naught; nor was that august personage, Nicholas Vedder himself, sacred from the daring tongue of this terrible virago, who charged him outright with encouraging her husband in habits of idleness.

Poor Rip was at last reduced almost to despair; and his only alternative, to escape from the labor of the farm and the clamor of his wife, was to take gun in hand and stroll away into the woods. Here he would sometimes seat himself at the foot of a tree, and share the contents of his wallet with Wolf, with whom he sympathized as a fellow-sufferer in persecution. "Poor Wolf," he would say, "thy mistress leads thee a dog's life of it; but never mind, my lad, whilst I live thou shalt never want a friend to stand by thee!" Wolf would wag his tail, look wistfully in his master's face, and, if dogs can feel pity, I verily believe he reciprocated the sentiment with all his heart.

In a long ramble of the kind on a fine autumnal day, Rip had unconsciously scrambled to one of the highest parts of the Catskill **Mountains**.   He was after his favorite sport of squirrel shooting, and the still solitudes had echoed and reëchoed with the reports of his gun.   Panting and fatigued, he threw himself, late in the afternoon, on a green knoll, covered with mountain herbage, that crowned the brow of a precipice.   From an opening between the trees he could overlook all the lower country for many a mile of rich woodland.   He saw at a distance the lordly Hudson, far, far below him, moving on its silent but majestic course, with the reflection of a purple cloud, or the sail of a lagging bark, here and there sleeping on its glassy bosom, and at last losing itself in the blue highlands.

On the other side he looked down into a deep mountain glen, wild, lonely, and shagged, the bottom filled with fragments from the impending cliffs, and scarcely lighted by the reflected rays of the setting sun.   For some time Rip lay musing on this scene. Evening was gradually advancing ; the mountains began to throw their long, blue shadows over the valleys ; he saw that it would be dark long before he could reach the village, and he heaved a heavy sigh when he thought of encountering the terrors of Dame Van Winkle.

As he was about to descend, he heard a voice from a distance, hallooing, " Rip Van Winkle!   Rip Van Winkle!"   He looked around, but could see nothing but a crow winging its solitary flight across the mountain.   He thought his fancy must have deceived him, and turned again to descend, when he heard the same cry ring through the still evening air, " Rip Van Winkle! Rip Van Winkle!"   At the same time Wolf bristled up his back, and, giving a low growl, skulked to his master's side, looking fearfully down into the glen.   Rip now felt a vague apprehension stealing over him.   He looked anxiously in the same direction, and perceived a strange figure slowly toiling up the rocks, and bending under the weight of something he carried on his back.   He was surprised to see any human being in this lonely and unfrequented place, but, supposing it to be some one of the neighborhood in need of his assistance, he hastened down to yield it.

On nearer approach he was still more surprised at the singularity of the stranger's appearance. He was a short, square-built old fellow, with thick, bushy hair, and a grizzled beard. His dress was of the antique Dutch fashion, — a cloth jerkin[1] strapped round the waist; several pair of breeches, the outer one of ample volume, decorated with rows of buttons down the sides, and bunches at the knees. He bore on his shoulders a stout keg, that seemed full of liquor, and made signs for Rip to approach and assist him with the load. Though rather shy and distrustful of this new acquaintance, Rip complied with his usual alacrity; and, mutually relieving each other, they clambered up a narrow gully, apparently the dry bed of a mountain torrent. As they ascended, Rip every now and then heard long, rolling peals, like distant thunder, that seemed to issue out of a deep ravine, or rather cleft, between lofty rocks, toward which their rugged path conducted. He paused for an instant, but, supposing it to be the muttering of one of those transient thunder-showers which often take place in mountain heights, he proceeded. Passing through the ravine, they came to a hollow, like a small amphitheater, surrounded by perpendicular precipices, over the brinks of which impending trees shot their branches, so that you only caught glimpses of the azure sky and the bright evening cloud. During the whole time, Rip and his companion had labored on in silence; for, though the former marveled greatly what could be the object of carrying a keg of liquor up this wild mountain, yet there was something strange and incomprehensible about the unknown, that inspired awe and checked familiarity.

On entering the amphitheater, new objects of wonder presented themselves. On a level spot in the center was a company of odd-looking personages playing at ninepins. They were dressed in a quaint, outlandish fashion. Some wore short doublets;[2] others, jerkins, with long knives in their belts; and most of them

---

[1] A close jacket much worn in the sixteenth and seventeenth centuries.

[2] A close fitting outer garment, covering the body from the neck to below the waist.

had enormous breeches, of similar style with that of the guide's. Their visages, too, were peculiar. One had a large head, broad face, and small, piggish eyes. The face of another seemed to consist entirely of nose, and was surmounted by a white sugar-loaf hat, set off with a little red cock's tail. They all had beards, of various shapes and colors. There was one who seemed to be the commander. He was a stout old gentleman, with a weather-beaten countenance. He wore a laced doublet, broad belt and hanger,[1] high-crowned hat and feather, red stockings, and high-heeled shoes with roses in them. The whole group reminded Rip of the figures in an old Flemish painting in the parlor of Domi-nie Van Schaick, the village parson, and which had been brought over from Holland at the time of the settlement.

What seemed particularly odd to Rip was, that, though these folks were evidently amusing themselves, yet they maintained the gravest faces, the most mysterious silence, and were, withal, the most melancholy party of pleasure he had ever witnessed. Noth-ing interrupted the stillness of the scene but the noise of the balls, which, whenever they were rolled, echoed along the mountains like rumbling peals of thunder.

As Rip and his companion approached them, they suddenly desisted from their play, and stared at him with such fixed, statue-like gaze, and such strange, uncouth, lack-luster counte-nances, that his heart turned within him, and his knees smote to-gether. His companion now emptied the contents of the keg into large flagons, and made signs to him to wait upon the com-pany. He obeyed with fear and trembling. They quaffed the liquor in profound silence, and then returned to their game.

By degrees Rip's awe and apprehension subsided. He even ventured, when no eye was fixed upon him, to taste the bever-age, which he found had much of the flavor of excellent Hol-lands.[2] He was naturally a thirsty soul, and was soon tempted

---

[1] A short broadsword worn from the girdle. and slightly curved at the point.

[2] Holland gin.

to repeat the draught.   One taste provoked another; and he reiterated his visits to the flagon so often, that at length his senses
were overpowered, his eyes swam in his head, his head gradually
declined, and he fell into a deep sleep.

On waking, he found himself on the green knoll whence he had
first seen the old man of the glen.   He rubbed his eyes.   It was
a bright, sunny morning.   The birds were hopping and twittering among the bushes; and the eagle was wheeling aloft, and
breasting the pure mountain breeze.   "Surely," thought Rip,
"I have not slept here all night."   He recalled the occurrences
before he fell asleep,— the strange man with a keg of liquor,
the mountain ravine, the wild retreat among the rocks, the
woe-begone party at ninepins, the flagon.   "Oh, that wicked
flagon!" thought Rip: "what excuse shall I make to Dame
Van Winkle!"

He looked round for his gun, but in place of the clean, well-
oiled fowling-piece, he found an old firelock lying by him, the
barrel incrusted with rust, the lock falling off, and the stock
worm-eaten.   He now suspected that the grave roysters of the
mountain had put a trick upon him, and, having dosed him with
liquor, had robbed him of his gun.   Wolf, too, had disappeared;
but he might have strayed away after a squirrel or partridge.
He whistled after him, and shouted his name, but all in vain:
the echoes repeated his whistle and shout, but no dog was to
be seen.

He determined to revisit the scene of the last evening's gam-
bol, and, if he met with any of the party, to demand his dog and
gun.   As he rose to walk, he found himself stiff in the joints, and
wanting in his usual activity.   "These mountain beds do not
agree with me," thought Rip; "and, if this frolic should lay me
up with a fit of the rheumatism, I shall have a blessed time with
Dame Van Winkle."   With some difficulty he got down into the
glen.   He found the gully up which he and his companion had
ascended the preceding evening; but, to his astonishment, a
mountain stream was now foaming down it, leaping from rock to

rock, and filling the glen with babbling murmurs. He, however, made shift to scramble up its sides, working his toilsome way through thickets of birch, sassafras, and witch-hazel, and sometimes tripped up or entangled by the wild grape-vines that twisted their coils and tendrils from tree to tree, and spread a kind of network in his path.

At length he reached to where the ravine had opened through the cliffs to the amphitheater; but no traces of such opening remained. The rocks presented a high, impenetrable wall, over which the torrent came tumbling in a sheet of feathery foam, and fell into a broad, deep basin, black from the shadows of the surrounding forest. Here, then, poor Rip was brought to a stand. He again called and whistled after his dog. He was only answered by the cawing of a flock of idle crows, sporting high in air about a dry tree that overhung a sunny precipice, and who, secure in their elevation, seemed to look down and scoff at the poor man's perplexities. What was to be done? The morning was passing away, and Rip felt famished for want of his breakfast. He grieved to give up his dog and gun, he dreaded to meet his wife; but it would not do to starve among the mountains. He shook his head, shouldered the rusty firelock, and, with a heart full of trouble and anxiety, turned his steps homeward.

As he approached the village, he met a number of people, but none whom he knew; which somewhat surprised him, for he had thought himself acquainted with every one in the country round. Their dress, too, was of a different fashion from that to which he was accustomed. They all stared at him with equal marks of surprise, and, whenever they cast their eyes upon him, invariably stroked their chins. The constant recurrence of this gesture induced Rip involuntarily to do the same, when, to his astonishment, he found his beard had grown a foot long.

He had now entered the skirts of the village. A troop of strange children ran at his heels, hooting after him, and pointing at his gray beard. The dogs, too, not one of which he recognized for an old acquaintance, barked at him as he passed. The very village was altered: it was larger and more populous. There were rows of houses which he had never seen before, and those which had been his familiar haunts had disappeared. Strange names were over the doors, strange faces at the windows: everything was strange. His mind now misgave him. He began to doubt whether both he and the world around him were not bewitched. Surely this was his native village, which he had left but the day before. There stood the Catskill Mountains; there ran the silver Hudson at a distance; there was every hill and dale precisely as it had always been. Rip was sorely perplexed. "That flagon last night," thought he, "has addled my poor head sadly."

It was with some difficulty that he found the way to his own house, which he approached with silent awe, expecting every moment to hear the shrill voice of Dame Van Winkle. He found the house gone to decay, — the roof fallen in, the windows shattered, and the doors off the hinges. A half-starved dog that looked like Wolf was skulking about it. Rip called him by name; but the cur snarled, showed his teeth, and passed on. This was an unkind cut, indeed. "My very dog," sighed poor Rip, "has forgotten me!"

He entered the house, which, to tell the truth, Dame Van Winkle had always kept in neat order. It was empty, forlorn, and apparently abandoned. This desolateness overcame all his connubial fears. He called loudly for his wife and children: the lonely chambers rang for a moment with his voice, and then all again was silence.

He now hurried forth, and hastened to his old resort, the village inn; but it, too, was gone. A large, rickety, wooden building stood in its place, with great, gaping windows, some of them broken and mended with old hats and petticoats; and over the door was painted, "The Union Hotel, by Jonathan Doolittle." Instead of the great tree that used to shelter the quiet little Dutch inn of yore, there now was reared a tall, naked pole, with something on the top that looked like a red night-cap;[1] and from it was fluttering a flag, on which was a singular assemblage of stars and stripes. All this was strange and incomprehensible. He recognized on the sign, however, the ruby face of King George, under which he had smoked so many a peaceful pipe; but even this was singularly metamorphosed. The red coat was changed for one of blue and buff, a sword was held in the hand instead of a scepter, the head was decorated with a cocked hat, and underneath was painted in large characters, "General Washington."

There was, as usual, a crowd of folk about the door, but none that Rip recollected. The very character of the people seemed changed. There was a busy, bustling, disputatious tone about it, instead of the accustomed phlegm and drowsy tranquillity. He looked in vain for the sage Nicholas Vedder, with his broad face, double chin, and fair long pipe, uttering clouds of tobacco-smoke instead of idle speeches; or Van Bummel, the schoolmaster, doling forth the contents of an ancient newspaper. In place of these, a lean, bilious-looking fellow, with his pockets full of handbills, was haranguing vehemently about the rights of citizens, election, members of Congress, liberty, Bunker's Hill,[2] heroes of seventy-six, and other words, that were a perfect Babylonish jargon to the bewildered Van Winkle.

The appearance of Rip, with his long, grizzled beard, his rusty fowling-piece, his uncouth dress, and the army of women and children that had gathered at his heels, soon attracted the attention of the tavern politicians. They crowded round him, eying

[1] Cap of liberty worn in the Roman states by manumitted slaves. It was made thus according to a coin of Brutus after the death of Cæsar, and worn by Brutus and his rebels, as a token of their *republican* sentiment. Its shape was copied from the Phrygian cap, which had become a symbol or emblem of personal and political freedom.

[2] A celebrated height in Charlestown, Mass. (now a part of Boston), famous as the place where a battle was fought between the British and American forces June 17, 1775.

him from head to foot with great curiosity. The orator bustled up to him, and, drawing him partly aside, inquired on which side he voted. Rip stared in vacant stupidity. Another short but busy little fellow pulled him by the arm, and, rising on tiptoe, inquired in his ear whether he was a Federal or a Democrat. Rip was equally at a loss to comprehend the question, when a knowing, self-important old gentleman in a sharp cocked hat made his way through the crowd, putting them to the right and left with his elbows as he passed, and, planting himself before Van Winkle, — with one arm akimbo, the other resting on his cane; his keen eyes and sharp hat penetrating, as it were, into his very soul, — demanded in an austere tone what brought him to the election with a gun on his shoulder and a mob at his heels, and whether he meant to breed a riot in the village. "Alas! gentlemen," cried Rip, somewhat dismayed, "I am a poor, quiet man, a native of the place, and a loyal subject to the King, God bless him!"

Here a general shout burst from the bystanders: "A Tory, a Tory! A spy! A refugee! Hustle him! Away with him!" It was with great difficulty that the self-important man in the cocked hat restored order, and, having assumed a tenfold austerity of brow, demanded again of the unknown culprit what he came there for, and whom he was seeking. The poor man humbly assured him that he meant no harm, but merely came there in search of some of his neighbors, who used to keep about the tavern.

"Well, who are they? Name them."

Rip bethought himself a moment, and inquired, "Where's Nicholas Vedder?"

There was a silence for a little while, when an old man replied in a thin, piping voice, "Nicholas Vedder! Why, he is dead and gone these eighteen years! There was a wooden tombstone in the churchyard that used to tell all about him, but that's rotten and gone, too."

"Where's Brom Dutcher?"

"Oh, he went off to the army in the beginning of the war

Some say he was killed at the storming of Stony Point;[1] others
say he was drowned in the squall at the foot of Anthony's Nose.[2]
I don't know: he never came back again."

"Where's Van Bummel, the schoolmaster?"

"He went off to the wars, too, was a great militia general, and
is now in Congress."

Rip's heart died away at hearing of these sad changes in his
home and friends, and finding himself thus alone in the world.
Every answer puzzled him, too, by treating of such enormous
lapses of time, and of matters which he could not understand,—
war, Congress, Stony Point. He had no courage to ask after
any more friends, but cried out in despair, "Does nobody here
know Rip Van Winkle?"

"Oh, Rip Van Winkle!" exclaimed two or three. "Oh, to
be sure! that's Rip Van Winkle yonder, leaning against the
tree."

Rip looked, and beheld a precise counterpart of himself, as he
went up the mountain, apparently as lazy, and certainly as ragged. The poor fellow was now completely confounded. He
doubted his own identity, and whether he was himself or another
man. In the midst of his bewilderment, the man in the cocked
hat demanded who he was, and what was his name.

"God knows!" exclaimed he, at his wits' end. "I'm not myself: I'm somebody else. That's me yonder. No, that's somebody else got into my shoes. I was myself last night: but I fell
asleep on the mountain; and they've changed my gun; and
everything's changed; and I'm changed; and I can't tell what's
my name, or who I am!"

The bystanders began now to look at each other, nod, wink

---

[1] The well-known promontory on the Hudson River, forty-two miles
north of New York, where, July 16, 1779, Gen. "Mad Anthony" Wayne
took by storm the fort upon its rocky heights.

[2] Anthony's or St. Anthony's Nose is a headland fifty-seven miles from
New York, on the east side of the Hudson, in Putnam County. It juts from
the south side of Breakneck Hill at the north entrance of the Highlands.

significantly, and tap their fingers against their foreheads. There was a whisper, also, about securing the gun, and keeping the old fellow from doing mischief, at the very suggestion of which the self-important man in the cocked hat retired with some precipitation. At this critical moment a fresh, comely woman pressed through the throng to get a peep at the gray-bearded man. She had a chubby child in her arms, which, frightened at his looks, began to cry. "Hush, Rip!" cried she. "Hush, you little fool! The old man won't hurt you."

The name of the child, the air of the mother, the tone of her voice, all awakened a train of recollections in his mind. "What is your name, my good woman?" asked he.

"Judith Gardenier."

"And your father's name?"

"Ah, poor man, his name was Rip Van Winkle. It's twenty years since he went away from home with his gun, and never has been heard of since. His dog came home without him; but whether he shot himself, or was carried away by the Indians, nobody can tell. I was then but a little girl."

Rip had but one question more to ask, but he put it with a faltering voice: —

"Where's your mother?"

Oh, she too had died but a short time since. She broke a blood-vessel in a fit of passion at a New England peddler.

There was a drop of comfort, at least, in this intelligence. The honest man could contain himself no longer. He caught his daughter and her child in his arms. "I am your father!" cried he, — "young Rip Van Winkle once, old Rip Van Winkle now! Does nobody know poor Rip Van Winkle?"

All stood amazed, until an old woman, tottering out from among the crowd, put her hand to her brow, and, peering under it in his face for a moment, exclaimed, "Sure enough! It is Rip Van Winkle! It is himself! Welcome home again, old neighbor! Why, where have you been these twenty long years?"

Rip's story was soon told, for the whole twenty years had been

to him but as one night.   The neighbors stared when they heard
it.   Some were seen to wink at each other, and put their tongues
in their cheeks; and the self-important man in the cocked hat,
who, when the alarm was over, had returned to the field, screwed
down the corners of his mouth, and shook his head, upon which
there was a general shaking of the head throughout the assemblage.

It was determined, however, to take the opinion of old Peter
Vanderdonk, who was seen slowly advancing up the road.   He
was a descendant of the historian of that name, who wrote one
of the earliest accounts of the province.   Peter was the most ancient inhabitant of the village, and well versed in all the wonderful events and traditions of the neighborhood.   He recollected
Rip at once, and corroborated his story in the most satisfactory
manner.   He assured the company that it was a fact, handed
down from his ancestor the historian, that the Catskill Mountains
had always been haunted by strange beings; that it was affirmed
that the great Hendrick Hudson,[1] the first discoverer of the river
and country, kept a kind of vigil there every twenty years, with his
crew of the Half-moon,[2] being permitted in this way to revisit the
scenes of his enterprise, and keep a guardian eye upon the river,
and the great city called by his name; that his father had once
seen them in their old Dutch dresses, playing at ninepins in the hollow of the mountain; and that he himself had heard, one summer
afternoon, the sound of their balls, like distant peals of thunder.

To make a long story short, the company broke up, and returned to the more important concerns of the election.   Rip's
daughter took him home to live with her.   She had a snug, well-
furnished house, and a stout, cheery farmer for a husband, whom
Rip recollected for one of the urchins that used to climb upon his
back.   As to Rip's son and heir, who was the ditto of himself,
seen leaning against the tree, he was employed to work on the
farm, but evinced an hereditary disposition to attend to anything
else but his business.

1 See Note 1, p. 96.   2 Hendrick Hudson's ship.

Rip now resumed his old walks and habits. He soon found many of his former cronies, though all rather the worse for the wear and tear of time, and preferred making friends among the rising generation, with whom he soon grew into great favor.

Having nothing to do at home, and being arrived at that happy age when a man can do nothing with impunity, he took his place once more on the bench at the inn door, and was reverenced as one of the patriarchs of the village, and a chronicle of the old times "before the war." It was some time before he could get into the regular track of gossip, or could be made to comprehend the strange events that had taken place during his torpor, — how that there had been a revolutionary war; that the country had thrown off the yoke of old England, and that, instead of being a subject of his Majesty George III., he was now a free citizen of the United States. Rip, in fact, was no politician, — the changes of states and empires made but little impression on him, — but there was one species of despotism under which he had long groaned, and that was, petticoat government. Happily, that was at an end. He had got his neck out of the yoke of matrimony, and could go in and out whenever he pleased, without dreading the tyranny of Dame Van Winkle. Whenever her name was mentioned, however, he shook his head, shrugged his shoulders, and cast up his eyes; which might pass either for an expression of resignation to his fate, or joy at his deliverance.

He used to tell his story to every stranger that arrived at Mr. Doolittle's hotel. He was observed at first to vary on some points every time he told it, which was doubtless owing to his having so recently awaked. It at last settled down precisely to the tale I have related; and not a man, woman, or child in the neighborhood but knew it by heart. Some always pretended to doubt the reality of it, and insisted that Rip had been out of his head, and that this was one point on which he always remained flighty. The old Dutch inhabitants, however, almost universally gave it full credit. Even to this day they never hear a thunder-

storm of a summer afternoon about the Catskill, but they say
Hendrick Hudson and his crew are at their game of ninepins;
and it is a common wish of all hen-pecked husbands in the neighborhood, when life hangs heavy on their hands, that they might
have a quieting draught out of Rip Van Winkle's flagon.

NOTE.

THE foregoing tale, one would suspect, had been suggested to Mr. Knickerbocker by a little German superstition about the Emperor Frederick *der Roth-
bart* and the Kyphäuser Mountain; the subjoined note, however, which he
had appended to the tale, shows that it is an absolute fact, narrated with his
usual fidelity.

"The story of Rip Van Winkle may seem incredible to many; but nevertheless I give it my full belief, for I know the vicinity of our old Dutch
settlements to have been very subject to marvelous events and appearances.
Indeed, I have heard many stranger stories than this, in the villages along
the Hudson, all of which were too well authenticated to admit of a doubt.
I have even talked with Rip Van Winkle myself, who, when last I saw him,
was a very venerable old man, and so perfectly rational and consistent on
every other point, that I think no conscientious person could refuse to take
this into the bargain; nay, I have seen a certificate on the subject taken before a country justice and signed with a cross, in the justice's own handwrit-
ing. The story, therefore, is beyond the possibility of doubt."

POSTSCRIPT.

The following are traveling notes from a memorandum-book of Mr.
Knickerbocker : —

"The Kaatsberg, or Catskill Mountains, have always been a region full
of fable. The Indians considered them the abode of spirits, who influenced
the weather, spreading sunshine or clouds over the landscape, and sending
good or bad hunting seasons. They were ruled by an old squaw spirit, said
to be their mother. She dwelt on the highest peak of the Catskills, and had
charge of the doors of day and night to open and shut them at the proper
hour. She hung up the new moons in the skies, and cut up the old ones into
stars. In times of drought, if properly propitiated, she would spin light
summer clouds out of cobwebs and morning dew, and send them off from the
crest of the mountain, flake after flake, like flakes of carded cotton, to float in
the air; until, dissolved by the heat of the sun, they would fall in gentle

showers, causing the grass to spring, the fruits to ripen, and the corn to grow an inch an hour. If displeased, however, she would brew up clouds black as ink, sitting in the midst of them like a bottle-bellied spider in the midst of its web; and when these clouds broke, woe betide the valleys!

"In old times, say the Indian traditions, there was a kind of Monitou, or Spirit, who kept about the wildest recesses of the Catskill Mountains, and took a mischievous pleasure in wreaking all kinds of evils and vexations upon the redmen. Sometimes he would assume the form of a bear, a panther, or a deer, lead the bewildered hunter a weary chase through tangled forests and among ragged rocks, and then spring off with a loud ' ho, ho! ' leaving him aghast on the brink of a beetling precipice or raging torrent."

THE WIFE.

> " *The treasures of the deep are not so precious*
> *As are the conceal'd comforts of a man*
> *Locked up in woman's love. I scent the air*
> *Of blessings when I come but near the house.*
> *What a delicious breath marriage sends forth !*
> *The violet bed 's not sweeter.*"
>
> MIDDLETON.[1]

I HAVE often had occasion to remark the fortitude with which women sustain the most overwhelming reverses of fortune. Those disasters which break down the spirit of a man, and prostrate him in the dust, seem to call forth all the energies of the softer sex, and give such intrepidity and elevation to their character, that at times it approaches to sublimity. Nothing can be more touching than to behold a soft and tender female, who had been all weakness and dependence, and alive to every trivial roughness, while treading the prosperous paths of life, suddenly rising in mental force to be the comforter and support of her husband under misfortune, and abiding with unshrinking firmness the bitterest blasts of adversity.

[1] Thomas Middleton (about 1570–1627), an English dramatist. The above selection is from his play Women Beware Women, act iii. sc. I.

As the vine, which has long twined its graceful foliage about the oak, and been lifted by it into sunshine, will, when the hardy plant is rifted by the thunderbolt, cling round it with its caressing tendrils, and bind up its shattered boughs; so is it beautifully ordered by Providence, that woman, who is the mere dependent and ornament of man in his happier hours, should be his stay and solace when smitten with sudden calamity; winding herself into the rugged recesses of his nature, tenderly supporting the drooping head, and binding up the broken heart.

I was once congratulating a friend, who had around him a blooming family, knit together in the strongest affection. "I can wish you no better lot," said he, with enthusiasm, "than to have a wife and children.—If you are prosperous, there they are to share your prosperity; if otherwise, there they are to comfort you." And, indeed, I have observed that a married man falling into misfortune is more apt to retrieve his situation in the world than a single one; partly, because he is more stimulated to exertion by the necessities of the helpless and beloved beings who depend upon him for subsistence, but chiefly, because his spirits are soothed and relieved by domestic endearments, and his self-respect kept alive by finding, that though all abroad is darkness and humiliation, yet there is still a little world of love at home, of which he is the monarch. Whereas a single man is apt to run to waste and self-neglect; to fancy himself lonely and abandoned, and his heart to fall to ruin like some deserted mansion, for want of an inhabitant.

These observations call to mind a little domestic story, of which I was once a witness. My intimate friend, Leslie, had married a beautiful and accomplished girl, who had been brought up in the midst of fashionable life. She had, it is true, no fortune, but that of my friend was ample, and he delighted in the anticipation of indulging her in every elegant pursuit, and administering to those delicate tastes and fancies that spread a kind of witchery about the sex.—"Her life," said he, "shall be like a fairy tale."

The very difference in their characters produced an harmonious combination: he was of a romantic and somewhat serious cast; she was all life and gladness. I have often noticed the mute rapture with which he would gaze upon her in company, of which her sprightly powers made her the delight; and how, in the midst of applause, her eye would still turn to him, as if there alone she sought favor and acceptance. When leaning on his arm, her slender form contrasted finely with his tall, manly person. The fond, confiding air with which she looked up to him seemed to call forth a flush of triumphant pride and cherishing tenderness, as if he doted on his lovely burden for its very helplessness. Never did a couple set forward on the flowery path of early and well-suited marriage with a fairer prospect of felicity.

It was the misfortune of my friend, however, to have embarked his property in large speculations; and he had not been married many months, when, by a succession of sudden disasters, it was swept from him, and he found himself reduced almost to penury. For a time he kept his situation to himself, and went about with a haggard countenance and a breaking heart. His life was but a protracted agony; and what rendered it more insupportable was the necessity of keeping up a smile in the presence of his wife; for he could not bring himself to overwhelm her with the news. She saw, however, with the quick eyes of affection, that all was not well with him. She marked his altered looks and stifled sighs, and was not to be deceived by his sickly and vapid attempts at cheerfulness. She tasked all her sprightly powers and tender blandishments to win him back to happiness; but she only drove the arrow deeper into his soul. The more he saw cause to love her, the more torturing was the thought that he was soon to make her wretched. A little while, thought he, and the smile will vanish from that cheek—the song will die away from those lips—the luster of those eyes will be quenched with sorrow—and the happy heart which now beats lightly in that bosom will be weighed down, like mine, by the cares and miseries of the world.

At length he came to me one day, and related his whole situation in a tone of the deepest despair. When I heard him through I inquired, "Does your wife know all this?" At the question he burst into an agony of tears. "For God's sake!" cried he, "if you have any pity on me, don't mention my wife; it is the thought of her that drives me almost to madness!"

"And why not?" said I. "She must know it sooner or later: you cannot keep it long from her, and the intelligence may break upon her in a more startling manner than if imparted by yourself; for the accents of those we love soften the harshest tidings. Besides, you are depriving yourself of the comforts of her sympathy; and not merely that, but also endangering the only bond that can keep hearts together,—an unreserved community of thought and feeling. She will soon perceive that something is secretly preying upon your mind; and true love will not brook reserve; it feels undervalued and outraged when even the sorrows of those it loves are concealed from it."

"Oh, but, my friend! to think what a blow I am to give to all her future prospects,—how I am to strike her very soul to the earth by telling her that her husband is a beggar! that she is to forego all the elegancies of life—all the pleasures of society —to shrink with me into indigence and obscurity! To tell her that I have dragged her down from the sphere in which she might have continued to move in constant brightness—the light of every eye—the admiration of every heart! How can she bear poverty? she has been brought up in all the refinements of opulence. How can she bear neglect? she has been the idol of society. Oh! it will break her heart—it will break her heart!"

I saw his grief was eloquent, and I let it have its flow; for sorrow relieves itself by words. When his paroxysm had subsided, and he had relapsed into moody silence, I resumed the subject gently, and urged him to break his situation at once to his wife. He shook his head mournfully but positively.

"But how are you to keep it from her? It is necessary she should know it, that you may take the steps proper to the altera-ion of your circumstances. You must change your style of living—nay," observing a pang to pass across his countenance, 'don't let that afflict you. I am sure you have never placed your happiness in outward show,—you have yet friends, warm friends, who will not think the worse of you for being less splendidly lodged; and surely it does not require a palace to be happy with Mary—"

"I could be happy with her," cried he, convulsively, "in a hovel! I could go down with her into poverty and the dust! I could—I could—God bless her!—God bless her!" cried he, bursting into a transport of grief and tenderness.

"And believe me, my friend," said I, stepping up and grasping him warmly by the hand, "believe me, she can be the same with you. Aye, more: it will be a source of pride and triumph to her,—it will call forth all the latent energies and fervent sympathies of her nature; for she will rejoice to prove that she loves you for yourself. There is in every true woman's heart a spark of heavenly fire, which lies dormant in the broad daylight of prosperity, but which kindles up, and beams, and blazes in the dark hour of adversity. No man knows what the wife of his bosom is—no man knows what a ministering angel she is—until he has gone with her through the fiery trials of this world."

There was something in the earnestness of my manner, and the figurative style of my language, that caught the excited imagination of Leslie. I knew the auditor I had to deal with; and following up the impression I had made, I finished by persuading him to go home and unburden his sad heart to his wife.

I must confess, notwithstanding all I had said, I felt some little solicitude for the result. Who can calculate on the fortitude of one whose life has been a round of pleasures? Her gay spirits might revolt at the dark, downward path of low humility suddenly pointed out before her, and might cling to the sunny regions in which they had hitherto reveled. Besides, ruin in fashionable life is accompanied by so many galling mortifications, to which in other ranks it is a stranger. In short, I could not meet Leslie the next morning without trepidation. He had made the disclosure.

"And how did she bear it?"

"Like an angel! It seemed rather to be a relief to her mind, for she threw her arms round my neck, and asked if this was all that had lately made me unhappy. But, poor girl," added he, "she cannot realize the change we must undergo. She has no idea of poverty but in the abstract; she has only read of it in poetry, where it is allied to love. She feels as yet no privation; she suffers no loss of accustomed conveniences nor elegancies. When we come practically to experience its sordid cares, its paltry wants, its petty humiliations—then will be the real trial."

"But," said I, "now that you have got over the severest task, that of breaking it to her, the sooner you let the world into the secret the better. The disclosure may be mortifying; but then it is a single misery, and soon over: whereas you otherwise suffer it, in anticipation, every hour in the day. It is not poverty so much as pretense that harasses a ruined man—the struggle between a proud mind and an empty purse,—the keeping up a hollow show that must soon come to an end. Have the courage to appear poor, and you disarm poverty of its sharpest sting." On this point I found Leslie perfectly prepared. He had no false pride himself, and as to his wife, she was only anxious to conform to their altered fortunes.

Some days afterwards he called upon me in the evening. He had disposed of his dwelling house, and taken a small cottage in the country, a few miles from town. He had been busied all day in sending out furniture. The new establishment required few articles, and those of the simplest kind. All the splendid furniture of his late residence had been sold, excepting his wife's harp. That, he said, was too closely associated with the idea of herself; it belonged to the little story of their loves; for some of the sweetest moments of their courtship were those when he had leaned over that instrument and listened to the melting tones of her voice. I could not but smile at this instance of romantic gallantry in a doting husband.

He was now going out to the cottage, where his wife had been all day superintending its arrangement. My feelings had become strongly interested in the progress of this family story, and, as it was a fine evening, I offered to accompany him.

He was wearied with the fatigues of the day, and, as he walked out, fell into a fit of gloomy musing.

"Poor Mary!" at length broke, with a heavy sigh, from his lips.

"And what of her?" asked I. "Has anything happened to her?"

"What," said he, darting an impatient glance, "is it nothing to be reduced to this paltry situation—to be caged in a miserable cottage—to be obliged to toil almost in the menial concerns of her wretched habitation?"

"Has she then repined at the change?"

"Repined! she has been nothing but sweetness and good humor. Indeed, she seems in better spirits than I have ever known her; she has been to me all love, and tenderness, and comfort!"

"Admirable girl!" exclaimed I. "You call yourself poor, my friend; you never were so rich,—you never knew the boundless treasures of excellence you possess in that woman."

"Oh, but, my friend! if this first meeting at the cottage were over, I think I could then be comfortable. But this is her first day of real experience; she has been introduced into a humble dwelling,—she has been employed all day in arranging its miserable equipments,—she has, for the first time, known the fatigues of domestic employment,—she has, for the first time, looked round her on a home destitute of everything elegant—almost of everything convenient; and may now be sitting down, exhausted and spiritless, brooding over a prospect of future poverty."

There was a degree of probability in this picture that I could not gainsay, so we walked on in silence.

After turning from the main road up a narrow lane so thickly shaded with forest trees as to give it a complete air of seclusion, we came in sight of the cottage. It was humble enough in its appearance for the most pastoral poet; and yet it had a pleasing rural look. A wild vine had overrun one end with a profusion of foliage; a few trees threw their branches gracefully over it; and I observed several pots of flowers tastefully disposed about the door and on the grassplot in front. A small wicket gate opened upon a footpath that wound through some shrubbery to the door. Just as we approached, we heard the sound of music. Leslie grasped my arm; we paused and listened. It was Mary's voice singing, in a style of the most touching simplicity, a little air of which her husband was peculiarly fond.

I felt Leslie's hand tremble on my arm. He stepped forward to hear more distinctly. His step made a noise on the gravel walk. A bright, beautiful face glanced out at the window and vanished—a light footstep was heard—and Mary came tripping forth to meet us. She was in a pretty rural dress of white; a few wild flowers were twisted in her fine hair; a fresh bloom was on her cheek; her whole countenance beamed with smiles—I had never seen her look so lovely.

"My dear George," cried she, "I am so glad you are come! I have been watching and watching for you; and running down the lane, and looking out for you. I 've set out a table under a beautiful tree behind the cottage; and I 've been gathering some of the most delicious strawberries, for I know you are fond of them—and we have such excellent cream—and everything is so sweet and still here.—Oh!" said she, putting her arm within his, and looking up brightly in his face, "Oh, we shall be so happy!"

Poor Leslie was overcome. He caught her to his bosom—he folded his arms round her—he kissed her again and again; he could not speak, but the tears gushed into his eyes; and he has often assured me that, though the world has since gone prosperously with him, and his life has, indeed, been a happy one, yet never has he experienced a moment of more exquisite felicity.

THE ART OF BOOK-MAKING.

" If that severe doom of Synesius[1] be true, — ' It is a greater offence to steal dead men's labor than their clothes,'—what shall become of most writers?"
                                                    BURTON's Anatomy of Melancholy.[2]

I HAVE often wondered at the extreme fecundity of the press, and how it comes to pass that so many heads, on which nature seemed to have inflicted the curse of barrenness, yet teem with voluminous productions. As a man travels on, however, in the journey of life, his objects of wonder daily diminish, and he is continually finding out some very simple cause for some great matter of marvel. Thus have I chanced, in my peregrinations about this great metropolis, to blunder upon a scene which unfolded to me some of the mysteries of the book-making craft, and at once put an end to my astonishment.

I was one summer's day loitering through the great saloons of the British Museum,[3] with that listlessness with which one is apt to saunter about a room in warm weather; sometimes lolling over the glass cases of minerals, sometimes studying the hieroglyphics on an Egyptian mummy, and sometimes trying, with nearly equal success, to comprehend the allegorical paintings on the lofty ceilings. Whilst I was gazing about in this idle way, my attention was attracted to a distant door, at the end of a suite of apartments. It was closed, but every now and then it would open, and some strange-favored being, generally clothed in black, would steal forth, and glide through the rooms, without noticing any of the surrounding objects. There

---

1 Synesius (378–430 A.D.), bishop of Ptolemais, was a philosopher and writer.

2 This famous work by Robert Burton (1577–1640) was published in England in 1621.

3 A celebrated museum in London, founded in 1753. It contains famous collections of antiquities, drawings, prints, and an immense library.

was an air of mystery about this that piqued my languid curiosity, and I determined to attempt the passage of that strait, and to explore the unknown regions beyond. The door yielded to my hand, with all that facility with which the portals of enchanted castles yield to the adventurous knight-errant. I found myself in a spacious chamber, surrounded with great cases of venerable books. Above the cases, and just under the cornice, were arranged a great number of quaint black-looking portraits of ancient authors. About the room were placed long tables, with stands for reading and writing, at which sat many pale, cadaverous personages, poring intently over dusty volumes, rummaging among moldy manuscripts, and taking copious notes of their contents. The most hushed stillness reigned through this mysterious apartment, excepting that you might hear the racing of pens over sheets of paper, or occasionally the deep sigh of one of these sages as he shifted his position to turn over the page of an old folio, doubtless arising from that hollowness and flatulency incident to learned research.

Now and then one of these personages would write something on a small slip of paper, and ring a bell, whereupon a familiar would appear, take the paper in profound silence, glide out of the room, and return shortly loaded with ponderous tomes, upon which the other would fall tooth and nail with famished voracity. I had no longer a doubt that I had happened upon a body of magi, deeply engaged in the study of occult sciences. The scene reminded me of an old Arabian tale of a philosopher who was shut up in an enchanted library, in the bosom of a mountain, that opened only once a year; where he made the spirits of the place obey his commands, and bring him books of all kinds of dark knowledge, so that at the end of the year, when the magic portal once more swung open on its hinges, he issued forth so versed in forbidden lore as to be able to soar above the heads of the multitude, and to control the powers of nature.

My curiosity being now fully aroused, I whispered to one of the familiars, as he was about to leave the room, and begged an interpretation of the strange scene before me. A few words were sufficient for the purpose: — I found that these mysterious personages, whom I had mistaken for magi, were principally authors, and in the very act of manufacturing books. I was, in fact, in the reading room of the great British Library, — an immense collection of volumes of all ages and languages, many of which are now forgotten, and most of which are seldom read. To these sequestered pools of obsolete literature, therefore, do many modern authors repair, and draw buckets full of classic lore, or "pure English, undefiled," [1] wherewith to swell their own scanty rills of thought.

Being now in possession of the secret, I sat down in a corner and watched the process of this book manufactory. I noticed one lean, bilious-looking wight, who sought none but the most worm-eaten volumes, printed in black letter. He was evidently constructing some work of profound erudition, that would be purchased by every man who wished to be thought learned, placed upon a conspicuous shelf of his library, or laid open upon his table — but never read. I observed him, now and then, draw a large fragment of biscuit out of his pocket, and gnaw; whether it was his dinner, or whether he was endeavoring to keep off that exhaustion of the stomach produced by much pondering over dry works, I leave to harder students than myself to determine.

There was one dapper little gentleman in bright-colored clothes, with a chirping, gossiping expression of countenance, who had all the appearance of an author on good terms with his bookseller. After considering him attentively, I recognized in him a diligent getter-up of miscellaneous works, which bustled off well with the trade. I was curious to see how he manufactured his wares. He made more stir and show of business than any of the others; dipping into various books, fluttering over the leaves of manuscripts, taking a morsel out of one, a morsel

[1] See Edmund Spenser (1552–99), The Faerie Queene, Bk. IV. canto ii. stanza 32: "Well of English undefyled."

out of another, "line upon line, precept upon precept, here a little, and there a little." [1] The contents of his book seemed to be as heterogeneous as those of the witches' caldron in Macbeth.[2] It was here a finger and there a thumb, toe of frog and blind worm's sting, with his own gossip poured in like "baboon's blood," to make the medley "slab and good."

After all, thought I, may not this pilfering disposition be implanted in authors for wise purposes? May it not be the way in which Providence has taken care that the seeds of knowledge and wisdom shall be preserved from age to age in spite of the inevitable decay of the works in which they were first produced? We see that nature has wisely, though whimsically, provided for the conveyance of seeds from clime to clime, in the maws of certain birds; so that animals which, in themselves, are little better than carrion, and apparently the lawless plunderers of the orchard and the cornfield, are, in fact, nature's carriers to disperse and perpetuate her blessings.   In like manner, the beauties and fine thoughts of ancient and obsolete authors are caught up by these flights of predatory authors, and cast forth, again to flourish and bear fruit in a remote and distant tract of time. Many of their works, also, undergo a kind of metempsychosis, and spring up under new forms.   What was formerly a ponderous history revives in the shape of a romance—an old legend changes into a modern play—and a sober philosophical treatise furnishes the body for a whole series of bouncing and sparkling essays.   Thus it is in the clearing of our American woodlands; where we burn down a forest of stately pines, a progeny of dwarf oaks start up in their place; and we never see the prostrate trunk of a tree moldering into soil, but it gives birth to a whole tribe of fungi.

Let us not, then, lament over the decay and oblivion into which ancient writers descend; they do but submit to the great law of nature, which declares that all sublunary shapes of matter

[1] Isaiah xxviii. 10.
[2] See Shakespeare's Macbeth, act iv. sc. 1.

shall be limited in their duration, but which decrees, also, that their elements shall never perish. Generation after generation, both in animal and vegetable life, passes away, but the vital principle is transmitted to posterity, and the species continue to flourish. Thus, also, do authors beget authors, and having produced a numerous progeny, in a good old age they sleep with their fathers, that is to say, with the authors who preceded them —and from whom they had stolen.

Whilst I was indulging in these rambling fancies, I had leaned my head against a pile of reverend folios. Whether it was owing to the soporific emanations from these works; or to the profound quiet of the room; or to the lassitude arising from much wandering; or to an unlucky habit of napping at improper times and places, with which I am grievously afflicted, so it was that I fell into a doze. Still, however, my imagination continued busy, and indeed the same scene remained before my mind's eye, only a little changed in some of the details. I dreamt that the chamber was still decorated with the portraits of ancient authors, but that the number was increased. The long tables had disappeared, and, in place of the sage magi, I beheld a ragged, threadbare throng, such as may be seen plying about the great repository of cast-off clothes, Monmouth Street.[1] Whenever they seized upon a book, by one of those incongruities common to dreams, methought it turned into a garment of foreign or antique fashion, with which they proceeded to equip themselves. I noticed, however, that no one pretended to clothe himself from any particular suit, but took a sleeve from one, a cape from another, a skirt from a third, thus decking himself out piecemeal, while some of his original rags would peep out from among his borrowed finery.

There was a portly, rosy, well-fed parson, whom I observed ogling several moldy polemical writers through an eye-glass. He soon contrived to slip on the voluminous mantle of one of

---

[1] The market for second-hand wearing apparel in the eighteenth century in London.

the old fathers, and, having purloined the gray beard of another, endeavored to look exceedingly wise; but the smirking commonplace of his countenance set at naught all the trappings of wisdom. One sickly-looking gentleman was busied embroidering a very flimsy garment with gold thread drawn out of several old court dresses of the reign of Queen Elizabeth.[1] Another had trimmed himself magnificently from an illuminated manuscript, had stuck a nosegay in his bosom, culled from "The Paradise of Daintie Devices,"[2] and having put Sir Philip Sidney's[3] hat on one side of his head, strutted off with an exquisite air of vulgar elegance. A third, who was but of puny dimensions, had bolstered himself out bravely with the spoils from several obscure tracts of philosophy, so that he had a very imposing front; but he was lamentably tattered in rear, and I perceived that he had patched his small clothes with scraps of parchment from a Latin author.

There were some well-dressed gentlemen, it is true, who only helped themselves to a gem or so, which sparkled among their own ornaments, without eclipsing them. Some, too, seemed to contemplate the costumes of the old writers merely to imbibe their principles of taste, and to catch their air and spirit; but I grieve to say that too many were apt to array themselves from top to toe in the patchwork manner I have mentioned. I shall not omit to speak of one genius, in drab breeches and gaiters, and an Arcadian[4] hat, who had a violent propensity to the pastoral, but whose rural wanderings had been confined to the classic haunts of Primrose Hill[5] and the solitudes of the Regent's Park.[5]

---

[1] See Note 1, p. 89.

[2] A collection of poems compiled in 1576 by Richard Edwards, an English dramatist and poet.

[3] An English writer and general (1554–86), author of the pastoral romance *Arcadia,* and a series of sonnets, Astrophel and Stella.

[4] In reference to the poet's ideal Arcadia, — the haunt of shepherds and shepherdesses.

[5] An eminence north of Regent's Park, one of the largest parks in London.

He had decked himself in wreaths and ribbands from all the old pastoral poets, and, hanging his head on one side, went about with a fantastical, lackadaisical air, "babbling about green fields." [1] But the personage that most struck my attention was a pragmatical old gentleman, in clerical robes, with a remarkably large and square, but bald head. He entered the room wheezing and puffing, elbowed his way through the throng with a look of sturdy self-confidence, and having laid hands upon a thick Greek quarto, clapped it upon his head, and swept majestically away in a formidable frizzled wig. In the height of this literary masquerade, a cry suddenly resounded from every side, of "Thieves! thieves!" I looked, and lo! the portraits about the wall became animated! The old authors thrust out, first a head, then a shoulder, from the canvas, looked down curiously, for an instant, upon the motley throng, and then descended with fury in their eyes, to claim their rifled property. The scene of scampering and hubbub that ensued baffles all description. The unhappy culprits endeavored in vain to escape with their plunder. On one side might be seen half a dozen old monks stripping a modern professor; on another, there was sad devastation carried into the ranks of modern dramatic writers. Beaumont and Fletcher,[2] side by side, raged round the field like Castor and Pollux,[3] and sturdy Ben Jonson[4] enacted more wonders than when a volunteer with the army in Flanders. As to the dapper little compiler of farragos, mentioned some time since, he had arrayed himself in as many patches and colors as Harlequin, and there was as fierce a contention of claimants

[1] See Shakespeare's Henry V., act ii. sc. 3.

[2] Francis Beaumont (1584–1616), an English dramatist and poet. He lived in intimate relations with his friend John Fletcher (1579–1625). They formed a literary partnership and collaborated in the production of numerous plays.

[3] Twin brothers in Greek and Roman mythology. They had many adventures together, and temples were erected to them as divinities.

[4] A famous English dramatist (1573?–1637). He served for a short time in his youth as a soldier in the Netherlands.

about him as about the dead body of Patroclus.[1]   I was grieved
to see many men, to whom I had been accustomed to look upon
with awe and reverence, fain to steal off with scarce a rag to
cover their nakedness.   Just then my eye was caught by the pragmatical old gentleman in the Greek grizzled wig, who was scram-
bling away in sore affright with half a score of authors in full
cry after him.   They were close upon his haunches; in a
twinkling off went his wig; at every turn some strip of raiment
was peeled away, until in a few moments, from his domineer-
ing pomp, he shrunk into a little, pursy "chopped bald shot,"[2]
and made his exit with only a few tags and rags fluttering at
his back.

There was something so ludicrous in the catastrophe of this
learned Theban that I burst into an immoderate fit of laughter,
which broke the whole illusion.   The tumult and the scuffle were
at an end.   The chamber resumed its usual appearance.   The
old authors shrunk back into their picture frames, and hung in
shadowy solemnity along the walls.   In short, I found myself
wide awake in my corner, with the whole assemblage of bookworms gazing at me with astonishment.   Nothing of the dream
had been real but my burst of laughter, a sound never before
heard in that grave sanctuary, and so abhorrent to the ears of
wisdom, as to electrify the fraternity.

The librarian now stepped up to me, and demanded whether I
had a card of admission.   At first I did not comprehend him,
but I soon found that the library was a kind of literary "preserve," subject to game laws, and that no one must presume to
hunt there without special license and permission.   In a word, I
stood convicted of being an arrant poacher, and was glad to make
a precipitate retreat, lest I should have a whole pack of authors
let loose upon me.

---

[1] A Greek warrior in Homer's Iliad, the friend of Achilles.   He is slain
by Hector, and the Greeks and Trojans fight for the possession of his body.
See Iliad, Bk. XVII.

[2] Henry IV., Part II. act iii. sc. 2.

STRATFORD-ON-AVON.[1]

" Thou soft-flowing Avon, by thy silver stream
Of things more than mortal sweet Shakespeare would dream.
The fairies by moonlight dance round his green bed,
For hallow'd the turf is which pillow'd his head."

GARRICK.[2]

TO a homeless man, who has no spot on this wide world which he can truly call his own, there is a momentary feeling of something like independence and territorial consequence when, after a weary day's travel, he kicks off his boots, thrusts his feet into slippers, and stretches himself before an inn fire. Let the world without go as it may; let kingdoms rise or fall, so long as he has the wherewithal to pay his bill, he is, for the time being, the very monarch of all he surveys. The armchair is his throne, the poker his scepter, and the little parlor, some twelve feet square, his undisputed empire. It is a morsel of certainty, snatched from the midst of the uncertainties of life; it is a sunny moment gleaming out kindly on a cloudy day; and he who has advanced some way on the pilgrimage of existence knows the importance of husbanding even morsels and moments of enjoyment. "Shall I not take mine ease in mine inn?"[3] thought I, as I gave the fire a stir, lolled back in my elbowchair, and cast a complacent look about the little parlor of the Red Horse, at Stratford-on-Avon.

The words of sweet Shakespeare were just passing through my mind as the clock struck midnight from the tower of the church in which he lies buried. There was a gentle tap at the door, and

---

[1] A town in Warwickshire, England, situated on the river Avon. It is famous as the birthplace of Shakespeare. Here may be seen Shakespeare's house, in which an interesting museum has been formed. Pilgrimages to this literary shrine are made yearly by large numbers of persons.

[2] David Garrick (1717-79), a celebrated English actor who was the author of a number of plays, odes, and epigrams. He was famous for his portrayals of Shakespearean characters.

[3] Henry IV., Part I. act iii. sc. 3.

a pretty chambermaid, putting in her smiling face, inquired, with a hesitating air, whether I had rung.   I understood it as a modest hint that it was time to retire.   My dream of absolute dominion was at an end; so abdicating my throne, like a prudent potentate, to avoid being deposed, and putting the Stratford Guide Book under my arm as a pillow companion, I went to bed, and dreamt all night of Shakespeare, the jubilee,[1] and David Garrick.

The next morning was one of those quickening mornings which we sometimes have in early spring; for it was about the middle of March.   The chills of a long winter had suddenly given way; the north wind had spent its last gasp; and a mild air came stealing from the west, breathing the breath of life into nature, and wooing every bud and flower to burst forth into fragrance and beauty.

I had come to Stratford on a poetical pilgrimage.   My first visit was to the house where Shakespeare was born, and where, according to tradition, he was brought up to his father's craft of wool-combing.   It is a small, mean-looking edifice of wood and plaster, a true nestling-place of genius, which seems to delight in hatching its offspring in by-corners.   The walls of its squalid chambers are covered with names and inscriptions in every language, by pilgrims of all nations, ranks, and conditions, from the prince to the peasant, and present a simple but striking instance of the spontaneous and universal homage of mankind to the great poet of nature.

The house is shown by a garrulous old lady, in a frosty red face, lighted up by a cold blue anxious eye, and garnished with artificial locks of flaxen hair, curling from under an exceedingly dirty cap.   She was peculiarly assiduous in exhibiting the relics with which this, like all other celebrated shrines, abounds.   There was the shattered stock of the very matchlock with which Shakespeare shot the deer on his poaching exploits.[2]   There, too, was

1 Commemoration exercises devised by David Garrick and held at Stratford, September, 1769.

2 See p. 172.

his tobacco box, which proves that he was a rival smoker of Sir Walter Raleigh ;[1] the sword also with which he played Hamlet ; and the identical lantern with which Friar Laurence [2] discovered Romeo and Juliet at the tomb!   There was an ample supply also of Shakespeare's mulberry tree, which seems to have as extraordinary powers of self-multiplication as the wood of the true cross, of which there is enough extant to build a ship of the line.

The most favorite object of curiosity, however, is Shakespeare's chair.   It stands in the chimney nook of a small gloomy chamber, just behind what was his father's shop.   Here he may many a time have sat when a boy, watching the slowly-revolving spit with all the longing of an urchin ; or of an evening, listening to the cronies and gossips of Stratford dealing forth churchyard tales and legendary anecdotes of the troublesome times of England.   In this chair it is the custom of every one that visits the house to sit : whether this be done with the hope of imbibing any of the inspiration of the bard I am at a loss to say ; I merely mention the fact ; and mine hostess privately assured me that, though built of solid oak, such was the fervent zeal of devotees that the chair had to be new bottomed at least once in three years.   It is worthy of notice also, in the history of this extraordinary chair, that it partakes something of the volatile nature of the Santa Casa of Loretto,[3] or the flying chair of the Arabian enchanter ; for though sold some few years since to a northern princess, yet, strange to tell, it has found its way back again to the old chimney corner.

I am always of easy faith in such matters, and am ever willing to be deceived, where the deceit is pleasant and costs nothing. I am therefore a ready believer in relics, legends, and local anecdotes of goblins and great men ; and would advise all travelers

---

[1] An English admiral, historian, and poet (1552–1618). He was credited with doing much to introduce the use of tobacco in England.

[2] Romeo and Juliet, act v. sc. 3.

[3] A famous pilgrimage shrine in the town of Loretto in Italy. The Santa Casa (" Holy House ") is reputed to be the house of the Virgin, transported by angels from Nazareth.

who travel for their gratification to be the same. What is it to
us whether these stories be true or false, so long as we can persuade ourselves into the belief of them, and enjoy all the charm
of the reality? There is nothing like resolute good-humored
credulity in these matters; and on this occasion I went even so
far as willingly to believe the claims of mine hostess to a lineal
descent from the poet, when, luckily for my faith, she put into
my hands a play of her own composition, which set all belief in
her consanguinity at defiance.

From the birthplace of Shakespeare a few paces brought me to
his grave. He lies buried in the chancel of the parish church, a
large and venerable pile, moldering with age, but richly ornamented. It stands on the banks of the Avon, on an embowered
point, and separated by adjoining gardens from the suburbs of the
town. Its situation is quiet and retired; the river runs murmuring at the foot of the churchyard, and the elms which grow upon
its banks droop their branches into its clear bosom. An avenue
of limes, the boughs of which are curiously interlaced, so as to
form in summer an arched way of foliage, leads up from the gate
of the yard to the church porch. The graves are overgrown
with grass; the gray tombstones, some of them nearly sunk into
the earth, are half covered with moss, which has likewise tinted
the reverend old building. Small birds have built their nests
among the cornices and fissures of the walls, and keep up a continual flutter and chirping; and rooks are sailing and cawing
about its lofty gray spire.

In the course of my rambles I met with the gray-headed
sexton, and accompanied him home to get the key of the
church. He had lived in Stratford, man and boy, for eighty
years, and seemed still to consider himself a vigorous man, with
the trivial exception that he had nearly lost the use of his legs for
a few years past. His dwelling was a cottage, looking out upon
the Avon and its bordering meadows; and was a picture of that
neatness, order, and comfort which pervade the humblest dwellings in this country. A low whitewashed room, with a stone

floor carefully scrubbed, served for parlor, kitchen, and hall. Rows of pewter and earthen dishes glittered along the dresser. On an old oaken table, well rubbed and polished, lay the family Bible and prayer book, and the drawer contained the family library, composed of about half a score of well-thumbed volumes. An ancient clock, that important article of cottage furniture, ticked on the opposite side of the room, with a bright warming pan hanging on one side of it, and the old man's horn-handled Sunday cane on the other. The fireplace, as usual, was wide and deep enough to admit a gossip knot within its jambs. In one corner sat the old man's granddaughter sewing, a pretty blue-eyed girl, —and in the opposite corner was a superannuated crony, whom he addressed by the name of John Ange, and who, I found, had been his companion from childhood. They had played together in infancy; they had worked together in manhood; they were now tottering about and gossiping away the evening of life; and in a short time they will probably be buried together in the neighboring churchyard. It is not often that we see two streams of existence running thus evenly and tranquilly side by side; it is only in such quiet "bosom scenes" of life that they are to be met with.

I had hoped to gather some traditional anecdotes of the bard from these ancient chroniclers; but they had nothing new to impart. The long interval during which Shakespeare's writing lay in comparative neglect has spread its shadow over history; and it is his good or evil lot that scarcely anything remains to his biographers but a scanty handful of conjectures.

The sexton and his companion had been employed as carpenters on the preparations for the celebrated Stratford jubilee, and they remembered Garrick, the prime mover of the fête, who superintended the arrangements, and who, according to the sexton, was "a short punch man, very lively and bustling." John Ange had assisted also in cutting down Shakespeare's mulberry tree, of which he had a morsel in his pocket for sale; no doubt a sovereign quickener of literary conception.

I was grieved to hear these two worthy wights speak very

dubiously of the eloquent dame who shows the Shakespeare house.
John Ange shook his head when I mentioned her valuable and
inexhaustible collection of relics, particularly her remains of the
mulberry tree; and the old sexton even expressed a doubt as to
Shakespeare having been born in her house. I soon discovered
that he looked upon her mansion with an evil eye, as a rival to
the poet's tomb; the latter having comparatively but few visitors.
Thus it is that historians differ at the very outset, and mere peb-
bles make the stream of truth diverge into different channels
even at the fountain head.

We approached the church through the avenue of limes, and
entered by a Gothic porch, highly ornamented with carved doors
of massive oak. The interior is spacious, and the architecture
and embellishments superior to those of most country churches.
There are several ancient monuments of nobility and gentry, over
some of which hang funeral escutcheons, and banners dropping
piecemeal from the walls. The tomb of Shakespeare is in the
chancel. The place is solemn and sepulchral. Tall elms wave
before the pointed windows, and the Avon, which runs at a short
distance from the walls, keeps up a low perpetual murmur. A
flat stone marks the spot where the bard is buried. There are
four lines inscribed on it, said to have been written by himself,
and which have in them something extremely awful. If they are
indeed his own, they show that solicitude about the quiet of the
grave which seems natural to fine sensibilities and thoughtful
minds.

> "Good friend, for Jesus' sake forbeare
> To dig the dust enclosed here.
> Blessed be he that spares these stones,
> And curst be he that moves my bones."

Just over the grave, in a niche of the wall, is a bust of Shakespeare, put up shortly after his death, and considered as a resem-
blance. The aspect is pleasant and serene, with a finely arched
forehead; and I thought I could read in it clear indications of
that cheerful, social disposition by which he was as much char-

acterized among his contemporaries as by the vastness of his genius. The inscription mentions his age at the time of his decease—fifty-three years; an untimely death for the world: for what fruit might not have been expected from the golden autumn of such a mind, sheltered as it was from the stormy vicissitudes of life, and flourishing in the sunshine of popular and royal favor!

The inscription on the tombstone has not been without its effect. It has prevented the removal of his remains from the bosom of his native place to Westminster Abbey, which was at one time contemplated. A few years since, also, as some laborers were digging to make an adjoining vault, the earth caved in, so as to leave a vacant space almost like an arch, through which one might have reached into his grave. No one, however, presumed to meddle with his remains, so awfully guarded by a malediction; and lest any of the idle or the curious, or any collector of relics, should be tempted to commit depredations, the old sexton kept watch over the place for two days, until the vault was finished and the aperture closed again. He told me that he had made bold to look in at the hole, but could see neither coffin nor bones—nothing but dust. It was something, I thought, to have seen the dust of Shakespeare.

Next to this grave are those of his wife, his favorite daughter, Mrs. Hall, and others of his family. On a tomb close by, also, is a full-length effigy of his old friend John Combe of usurious memory, on whom he is said to have written a ludicrous epitaph.[1] There are other monuments around, but the mind refuses to dwell on anything that is not connected with Shakespeare. His idea pervades the place—the whole pile seems but as his mausoleum. The feelings, no longer checked and thwarted by doubt, here indulge in perfect confidence: other traces of him may be false or dubious, but here is palpable evidence and absolute certainty. As I trod the sounding pavement, there was something intense and thrilling in the idea that, in very truth, the remains of Shake-

[1] John Combe's usury was the subject of the humorous epitaph which Shakespeare wrote for his friend.

speare were moldering beneath my feet. It was a long time
before I could prevail upon myself to leave the place; and as I
passed through the churchyard, I plucked a branch from one of
the yew trees, the only relic that I have brought from Stratford.

I had now visited the usual objects of a pilgrim's devotion,
but I had a desire to see the old family seat of the Lucys at
Charlecot, and to ramble through the park where Shakespeare, in
company with some of the roysters of Stratford, committed his
youthful offense of deer-stealing. In this harebrained exploit
we are told that he was taken prisoner, and carried to the keeper's
lodge, where he remained all night in doleful captivity. When
brought into the presence of Sir Thomas Lucy, his treatment must
have been galling and humiliating; for it so wrought upon his
spirit as to produce a rough pasquinade, which was affixed to the
park gate at Charlecot.[1]

This flagitious attack upon the dignity of the knight so incensed
him that he applied to a lawyer at Warwick to put the severity
of the laws in force against the rhyming deerstalker. Shakespeare
did not wait to brave the united puissance of a knight of the
shire and a country attorney. He forthwith abandoned the
pleasant banks of the Avon and his paternal trade; wandered
away to London; became a hanger-on to the theaters, then an
actor; and finally wrote for the stage; and thus, through the
persecution of Sir Thomas Lucy, Stratford lost an indifferent
wool-comber, and the world gained an immortal poet. He re-

---

[1] IRVING'S NOTE.—The following is the only stanza extant of this
lampoon:—

> "A parliament member, a justice of peace,
>   At home a poor scarecrow, at London an asse,
> If lowsie is Lucy, as some volke miscalle it,
>   Then Lucy is lowsie, whatever befall it.
>   He thinks himself great;
>   Yet an asse in his state,
> We allow by his ears but with asses to mate.
> If Lucy is lowsie, as some volke miscalle it,
>   Then sing lowsie Lucy, whatever befall it."

tained, however, for a long time, a sense of the harsh treatment of the Lord of Charlecot, and revenged himself in his writings, but in the sportive way of a good-natured mind. Sir Thomas is said to be the original Justice Shallow,[1] and the satire is slyly fixed upon him by the justice's armorial bearings, which, like those of the knight, had white luces [2] in the quarterings.

Various attempts have been made by his biographers to soften and explain away this early transgression of the poet; but I look upon it as one of those thoughtless exploits natural to his situation and turn of mind. Shakespeare, when young, had doubtless all the wildness and irregularity of an ardent, undisciplined, and undirected genius. The poetic temperament has naturally something in it of the vagabond. When left to itself it runs loosely and wildly, and delights in everything eccentric and licentious. It is often a turn-up of a die, in the gambling freaks of fate, whether a natural genius shall turn out a great rogue or a great poet; and had not Shakespeare's mind fortunately taken a literary bias, he might have as daringly transcended all civil, as he has all dramatic laws.

I have little doubt that, in early life, when running, like an unbroken colt, about the neighborhood of Stratford, he was to be found in the company of all kinds of odd, anomalous characters; that he associated with all the madcaps of the place, and was one of those unlucky urchins, at mention of whom old men shake their heads, and predict that they will one day come to the gallows. To him the poaching in Sir Thomas Lucy's park was doubtless like a foray to a Scottish knight, and struck his eager and as yet untamed imagination as something delightfully adventurous.[3]

[1] A pompous country justice in Shakespeare's Merry Wives of Windsor and King Henry IV., Part II. See p. 180.

[2] IRVING'S NOTE.—The luce is a pike or jack, and abounds in the Avon about Charlecot.

[3] IRVING'S NOTE.—A proof of Shakespeare's random habits and associates in his youthful days may be found in a traditionary anecdote, picked up at Stratford by the elder Ireland, and mentioned in his " Picturesque Views on the Avon."

The old mansion of Charlecot and its surrounding park still
remain in the possession of the Lucy family, and are peculiarly
interesting from being connected with this whimsical but eventful
circumstance in the scanty history of the bard. As the house
stood but little more than three miles' distance from Stratford, I
resolved to pay it a pedestrian visit, that I might stroll leisurely
through some of those scenes from which Shakespeare must have
derived his earliest ideas of rural imagery.

The country was yet naked and leafless; but English scenery
is always verdant, and the sudden change in the temperature of
the weather was surprising in its quickening effects upon the landscape. It was inspiring and animating to witness this first awak-
ening of spring; to feel its warm breath stealing over the senses;
to see the moist, mellow earth beginning to put forth the green
sprout and the tender blade; and the trees and shrubs, in their

About seven miles from Stratford lies the thirsty little market town of
Bedford, famous for its ale. Two societies of the village yeomanry used to
meet, under the appellation of the Bedford topers, and to challenge the lovers
of good ale of the neighboring villages to a contest of drinking. Among
others, the people of Stratford were called out to prove the strength of their
heads; and in the number of the champions was Shakespeare, who, in spite
of the proverb that "they who drink beer will think beer," was as true to
his ale as Falstaff to his sack. The chivalry of Stratford was staggered at
the first onset, and sounded a retreat while they had yet legs to carry them
off the field. They had scarcely marched a mile when, their legs failing
them, they were forced to lie down under a crab tree, where they passed
the night. It is still standing, and goes by the name of Shakespeare's tree.

In the morning his companions awaked the bard, and proposed returning
to Bedford; but he declined, saying he had had enough, having drank with

> "Piping Pebworth, Dancing Marston,
> Haunted Hilbro', Hungry Grafton,
> Dudging Exhall, Papist Wicksford,
> Beggarly Broom, and Drunken Bedford."

"The villages here alluded to," says Ireland, "still bear the epithets thus
given them: the people of Pebworth are still famed for their skill on the
pipe and tabor; Hillborough is now called Haunted Hillborough; and Graf-
ton is famous for the poverty of its soil."

reviving tints and bursting buds, giving the promise of returning
foliage and flower. The cold snowdrop, that little borderer on
the skirts of winter, was to be seen with its chaste white blossoms
in the small gardens before the cottages. The bleating of the
new-dropped lambs was faintly heard from the fields. The sparrow
twittered about the thatched eaves and budding hedges; the
robin threw a livelier note into his late querulous wintry strain;
and the lark, springing up from the reeking bosom of the meadow,
towered away into the bright fleecy cloud, pouring forth torrents
of melody. As I watched the little songster mounting up higher
and higher, until his body was a mere speck on the white bosom
of the cloud, while the ear was still filled with his music, it called
to mind Shakespeare's exquisite little song in " Cymbeline :" [1]

" Hark! hark! the lark at heaven's gate sings,
    And Phœbus 'gins arise,
His steeds to water at those springs,
    On chaliced flowers that lies;

" And winking Mary-buds begin
    To ope their golden eyes;
With everything that pretty is,
    My lady sweet, arise! "

Indeed, the whole country about here is poetic ground: everything is associated with the idea of Shakespeare. Every old cottage that I saw, I fancied into some resort of his boyhood, where
he had acquired his intimate knowledge of rustic life and manners, and heard those legendary tales and wild superstitions which
he has woven like witchcraft into his dramas. For in his time,
we are told, it was a popular amusement in winter evenings " to
sit round the fire, and tell merry tales of errant knights, queens,
lovers, lords, ladies, giants, dwarfs, thieves, cheaters, witches,
fairies, goblins, and friars." [2]

[1] Act ii. sc. 3.
[2] IRVING'S NOTE.—Scot, in his " Discoverie of Witchcraft," enumerates a
host of these fireside fancies. " And they have so fraid us with bull-beggars,

My route for a part of the way lay in sight of the Avon, which made a variety of the most fanciful doublings and windings through a wide and fertile valley; sometimes glittering from among willows which fringed its borders; sometimes disappearing among groves or beneath green banks; and sometimes rambling out into full view, and making an azure sweep round a slope of meadow land. This beautiful bosom of country is called the Vale of the Red Horse. A distant line of undulating blue hills seems to be its boundary, whilst all the soft intervening landscape lies in a manner enchained in the silver links of the Avon.

After pursuing the road for about three miles, I turned off into a footpath, which led along the borders of fields and under hedgerows to a private gate of the park; there was a stile, however, for the benefit of the pedestrian, there being a public right of way through the grounds. I delight in these hospitable estates, in which every one has a kind of property—at least as far as the footpath is concerned. It in some measure reconciles a poor man to his lot, and, what is more, to the better lot of his neighbor, thus to have parks and pleasure-grounds thrown open for his recreation. He breathes the pure air as freely, and lolls as luxuriously under the shade, as the lord of the soil; and if he has not the privilege of calling all that he sees his own, he has not, at the same time, the trouble of paying for it, and keeping it in order.

I now found myself among noble avenues of oaks and elms, whose vast size bespoke the growth of centuries. The wind sounded solemnly among their branches, and the rooks cawed from their hereditary nests in the tree tops. The eye ranged through a long lessening vista, with nothing to interrupt the view

spirits, witches, urchins, elves, hags, fairies, satyrs, pans, faunes, syrens, kit with the can sticke, tritons, centaurs, dwarfes, giantes, imps, calcars, conjurors, nymphes, changelings, incubus, Robin-good-fellow, the sporne, the mare, the man in the oke, the hellwaine, the fier drake, the puckle, Tom Thombe, hobgoblins, Tom Tumbler, boneless, and such other bugs, that we were afraid of our own shadowes."

but a distant statue, and a vagrant deer stalking like a shadow across the opening.

There is something about these stately old avenues that has the effect of Gothic architecture, not merely from the pretended similarity of form, but from their bearing the evidence of long duration, and of having had their origin in a period of time with which we associate ideas of romantic grandeur. They betoken also the long-settled dignity, and proudly concentrated independence of an ancient family; and I have heard a worthy but aristocratic old friend observe, when speaking of the sumptuous palaces of modern gentry, that "money could do much with stone and mortar, but, thank Heaven, there was no such thing as suddenly building up an avenue of oaks."

It was from wandering in early life among this rich scenery, and about the romantic solitudes of the adjoining park of Fullbroke, which then formed a part of the Lucy estate, that some of Shakespeare's commentators have supposed he derived his noble forest meditations of Jaques, and the enchanting woodland pictures in "As You Like It."[1] It is in lonely wanderings through such scenes that the mind drinks deep but quiet draughts of inspiration, and becomes intensely sensible of the beauty and majesty of nature. The imagination kindles into reverie and rapture; vague but exquisite images and ideas keep breaking upon it; and we revel in a mute and almost incommunicable luxury of thought. It was in some such mood, and perhaps under one of those very trees before me, which threw their broad shades over the grassy banks and quivering waters of the Avon, that the poet's fancy may have sallied forth into that little song which breathes the very soul of a rural voluptuary:

> " Under the greenwood tree,
> Who loves to lie with me,
> And tune his merry note
> Unto the sweet bird's throat,

[1] Act ii. sc. I.

> Come hither, come hither, come hither;
>   Here shall he see
>   No enemy,
>   But winter and rough weather." [1]

I had now come in sight of the house. It is a large building of brick, with stone quoins, and is in the Gothic style of Queen Elizabeth's day, having been built in the first year of her reign.[2] The exterior remains very nearly in its original state, and may be considered a fair specimen of the residence of a wealthy country gentleman of those days. A great gateway opens from the park into a kind of courtyard in front of the house, ornamented with a grassplot, shrubs, and flower beds. The gateway is in imitation of the ancient barbican, being a kind of outpost, and flanked by towers, though evidently for mere ornament instead of defence. The front of the house is completely in the old style, with stone-shafted casements, a great bow window of heavy stonework, and a portal with armorial bearings over it, carved in stone. At each corner of the building is an octagon tower, surmounted by a gilt ball and weathercock.

The Avon, which winds through the park, makes a bend just at the foot of a gently sloping bank, which sweeps down from the rear of the house. Large herds of deer were feeding or reposing upon its borders, and swans were sailing majestically upon its bosom. As I contemplated the venerable old mansion, I called to mind Falstaff's encomium on Justice Shallow's abode, and the affected indifference and real vanity of the latter.

Falstaff. You have a goodly dwelling and a rich.

Shallow. Barren, barren, barren; beggars all, beggars all, Sir John:—marry, good air.[3]

Whatever may have been the joviality of the old mansion in the days of Shakespeare, it had now an air of stillness and solitude. The great iron gateway that opened into the courtyard was

---

[1] As You Like It, act ii. sc. 5.

[2] 1558.   [3] Henry IV., Part II. act v. sc. 3.

locked; there was no show of servants bustling about the place; the deer gazed quietly at me as I passed, being no longer harried by the moss-troopers [1] of Stratford. The only sign of domestic life that I met with was a white cat, stealing with wary look and stealthy pace towards the stables, as if on some nefarious expedition. I must not omit to mention the carcass of a scoundrel crow which I saw suspended against the barn wall, as it shows that the Lucys still inherit that lordly abhorrence of poachers and maintain that rigorous exercise of territorial power which was so strenuously manifested in the case of the bard.

After prowling about for some time, I at length found my way to a lateral portal which was the every-day entrance to the mansion. I was courteously received by a worthy old housekeeper, who, with the civility and communicativeness of her order, showed me the interior of the house. The greater part has undergone alterations, and been adapted to modern tastes and modes of living: there is a fine old oaken staircase; and the great hall, that noble feature in an ancient manor house, still retains much of the appearance it must have had in the days of Shakespeare. The ceiling is arched and lofty, and at one end is a gallery in which stands an organ. The weapons and trophies of the chase, which formerly adorned the hall of a country gentleman, have made way for family portraits. There is a wide, hospitable fireplace, calculated for an ample old-fashioned wood fire, formerly the rallying place of winter festivity. On the opposite side of the hall is the huge Gothic bow window, with stone shafts, which looks out upon the courtyard. Here are emblazoned in stained glass the armorial bearings of the Lucy family for many generations, some being dated in 1558. I was delighted to observe in the quarterings the three *white luces* by which the character of Sir Thomas was first identified with that of Justice Shallow. They are mentioned in the first scene of the " Merry Wives of Windsor," where the Justice is in a rage with Falstaff

[1] Marauders; a term applied to men who troop or range over the mosses or bogs.

for having "beaten his men, killed his deer, and broken into his
lodge." The poet had no doubt the offences of himself and his
comrades in mind at the time, and we may suppose the family
pride and vindictive threats of the puissant Shallow to be a
caricature of the pompous indignation of Sir Thomas.

> *Shallow.* Sir Hugh, persuade me not; I will make a Star-Chamber [1]
> matter of it : if he were twenty Sir John Falstaffs, he shall not abuse Robert
> Shallow, Esquire.
> *Slender.* In the county of Glocester, Justice of Peace, and *coram*.[2]
> *Shallow.* Ay, cousin Slender, and *custalorum*.[3]
> *Slender.* Ay, and *ratolorum* [3] too ; and a gentleman born, Master Parson ;
> who writes himself *Armigero* [4] in any bill, warrant, quittance, or obligation,
> *Armigero.*
> *Shallow.* Ay, that I do ; and have done any time these three hundred
> years.
> *Slender.* All his successors, gone before him, hath done 't, and all his an-
> cestors that come after him may ; they may give the dozen *white luces* [5] in their
> coat. . . .
> *Shallow.* The Council shall hear it ; it is a riot.
> *Evans.* It is not meet the Council hear a riot ; there is no fear of Got
> in a riot. The Council, look you, shall desire to hear the fear of Got, and not
> to hear a riot ; take your vizaments in that.
> *Shallow.* Ha! o' my life, if I were young again, the sword should end
> it !

Near the window thus emblazoned hung a portrait by Sir
Peter Lely,[6] of one of the Lucy family, a great beauty of the
time of Charles II. The old housekeeper shook her head as
she pointed to the picture, and informed me that this lady had

---

[1] A court of civil and criminal jurisdiction at Westminster, so called because
the roof of the chamber was decorated with golden stars.

[2] Latin " in the presence of," used in legal phraseology. Slender blun-
deringly considers it an additional title to that of justice.

[3] Corruptions for *custos rotulorum*, " keeper of the records."

[4] Armiger ; a term used to designate one who had a right to armorial bearings.

[5] See note 2, p. 173.

[6] A famous Dutch artist (1618–80), court painter to Charles II. (1630–85).
His portraits of the beauties of Charles's court are celebrated.

been sadly addicted to cards, and had gambled away a great portion of the family estate, among which was that part of the park where Shakespeare and his comrades had killed the deer. The lands thus lost had not been entirely regained by the family even at the present day. It is but justice to this recreant dame to confess that she had a surpassingly fine hand and arm.

The picture which most attracted my attention was a great painting over the fireplace, containing likenesses of Sir Thomas Lucy and his family, who inhabited the hall in the latter part of Shakespeare's lifetime. I at first thought that it was the vindictive knight himself, but the housekeeper assured me that it was his son; the only likeness extant of the former being an effigy upon his tomb in the church of the neighboring hamlet of Charlecot. The picture gives a lively idea of the costume and manners of the time. Sir Thomas is dressed in ruff and doublet; white shoes with roses in them; and has a peaked yellow, or, as Master Slender would say, "a cane-colored beard." [1]   His lady is seated on the opposite side of the picture, in wide ruff and long stomacher, and the children have a most venerable stiffness and formality of dress. Hounds and spaniels are mingled in the family group; a hawk is seated on his perch in the foreground, and one of the children holds a bow,—all intimating the knight's skill in hunting, hawking, and archery—so indispensable to an accomplished gentleman in those days.

I regretted to find that the ancient furniture of the hall had disappeared; for I had hoped to meet with the stately elbow-chair of carved oak in which the country squire of former days was wont to sway the scepter of empire over his rural domains, and in which it might be presumed the redoubted Sir Thomas sat enthroned in awful state when the recreant Shakespeare was brought before him. As I like to deck out pictures for my own entertainment, I pleased myself with the idea that this very hall had been the scene of the unlucky bard's examination on the

[1] Merry Wives of Windsor, act i. sc. 4.

morning after his captivity in the lodge.   I fancied to myself the
rural potentate, surrounded by his bodyguard of butler, pages,
and blue-coated servingmen, with their badges; while the luck-
less culprit was brought in, forlorn and chapfallen, in the custody
of gamekeepers, huntsmen, and whippers-in, and followed by a
rabble rout of country clowns.   I fancied bright faces of curious
housemaids peeping from the half-opened doors; while from the
gallery the fair daughters of the knight leaned gracefully forward,
eying the youthful prisoner with that pity "that dwells in woman-
hood."—Who would have thought that this poor varlet, thus
trembling before the brief authority of a country squire and the
sport of rustic boors, was soon to become the delight of princes;
the theme of all tongues and ages; the dictator to the human
mind; and was to confer immortality on his oppressor by a caricature and a lampoon!

I was now invited by the butler to walk into the garden, and
I felt inclined to visit the orchard and arbor where the justice
treated Sir John Falstaff and Cousin Silence "to a last year's
pippin of his own graffing, with a dish of carraways;" [1] but I had
already spent so much of the day in my rambling that I was
obliged to give up any farther investigations.   When about to
take my leave, I was gratified by the civil entreaties of the housekeeper and butler that I would take some refreshment—an instance of good old hospitality which, I grieve to say, we castle-
hunters seldom meet with in modern days.   I make no doubt it
is a virtue which the present representative of the Lucys inherits
from his ancestors; for Shakespeare, even in his caricature, makes
Justice Shallow importunate in this respect, as witness his pressing instances to Falstaff:

"By cock and pye, sir, you shall not away to-night. . . . I will not excuse you; you shall not be excused; excuses shall not be admitted; there is
no excuse shall serve; you shall not be excused. . . . Some pigeons, Davy;
a couple of short-legged hens; a joint of mutton; and any pretty little tiny
kickshaws, tell William Cook." [2]

[1] Henry IV., Part II. act v. sc. 3.   [2] Ibid., act v. sc. 1.

I now bade a reluctant farewell to the old hall. My mind had become so completely possessed by the imaginary scenes and characters connected with it that I seemed to be actually living among them. Everything brought them, as it were, before my eyes; and as the door of the dining-room opened, I almost expected to hear the feeble voice of Master Silence quavering forth his favorite ditty :

> " 'T is merry in hall, when beards wag all,
> And welcome merry Shrove-tide!" [1]

On returning to my inn, I could not but reflect on the singular gift of the poet; to be able thus to spread the magic of his mind over the very face of nature; to give to things and places a charm and character not their own, and to turn this "working-day world" [2] into a perfect fairyland. He is indeed the true enchanter whose spell operates, not upon the senses, but upon the imagination and the heart. Under the wizard influence of Shakespeare I had been walking all day in a complete delusion. I had surveyed the landscape through the prism of poetry, which tinged every object with the hues of the rainbow. I had been surrounded with fancied beings, with mere airy nothings, conjured up by poetic power; yet which, to me, had all the charm of reality. I had heard Jaques soliloquize beneath his oak; had beheld the fair Rosalind and her companion adventuring through the woodlands; and, above all, had been once more present in spirit with fat Jack Falstaff and his contemporaries, from the august Justice Shallow down to the gentle Master Slender and the sweet Anne Page.[3] Ten thousand honors and blessings on the bard who has thus gilded the dull realities of life with innocent illusions; who has spread exquisite and unbought pleasures in my chequered path; and beguiled my spirit in many a lonely hour, with all the cordial and cheerful sympathies of social life!

As I crossed the bridge over the Avon on my return, I paused

---

[1] Henry IV., Part II. act v. sc. 3.   [2] As You Like It, act i. sc. 3.
[3] One of the characters in the Merry Wives of Windsor.

to contemplate the distant church in which the poet lies buried, and could not but exult in the malediction which has kept his ashes undisturbed in its quiet and hallowed vaults. What honor could his name have derived from being mingled in dusty companionship with the epitaphs and escutcheons and venal eulogiums of a titled multitude? What would a crowded corner in Westminster Abbey have been, compared with this reverend pile, which seems to stand in beautiful loneliness as his sole mausoleum! The solicitude about the grave may be but the offspring of an overwrought sensibility; but human nature is made up of foibles and prejudices; and its best and tenderest affections are mingled with these factitious feelings. He who has sought renown about the world, and has reaped a full harvest of worldly favor, will find, after all, that there is no love, no admiration, no applause, so sweet to the soul as that which springs up in his native place. It is there that he seeks to be gathered in peace and honor among his kindred and his early friends. And when the weary heart and failing head began to warn him that the evening of life is drawing on, he turns as fondly as does the infant to the mother's arms, to sink to sleep in the bosom of the scene of his childhood.

How would it have cheered the spirit of the youthful bard when, wandering forth in disgrace upon a doubtful world, he cast back a heavy look upon his paternal home, could he have foreseen that, before many years, he should return to it covered with renown; that his name should become the boast and glory of his native place; that his ashes should be religiously guarded as its most precious treasure; and that its lessening spire, on which his eyes were fixed in tearful contemplation, should one day become the beacon, towering amidst the gentle landscape, to guide the literary pilgrim of every nation to his tomb!

THE MUTABILITY OF LITERATURE.

[*A Colloquy in Westminster Abbey.*]

" I know that all beneath the moon decays,
And what by mortals in this world is brought,
In time's great periods shall return to nought.
I know that all the muses' heavenly layes,
With toil of sprite which are so dearly bought,
As idle sounds of few or none are sought,
 That there is nothing lighter than mere praise."
 DRUMMOND OF HAWTHORNDEN.[1]

THERE are certain half-dreaming moods of mind, in which we naturally steal away from noise and glare, and seek some quiet haunt, where we may indulge our reveries, and build our air castles undisturbed. In such a mood, I was loitering about the old gray cloisters of Westminster Abbey,[2] enjoying that luxury of wandering thought which one is apt to dignify with the name of reflection; when suddenly an irruption of mad-cap boys from Westminster School,[3] playing at football, broke in upon the monastic stillness of the place, making the vaulted passages and moldering tombs echo with their merriment. I sought to take refuge from their noise by penetrating still deeper into the solitudes of the pile, and applied to one of the vergers for admission to the library. He conducted me through a portal rich with the crumbling sculpture of former ages, which opened upon a gloomy passage leading to the Chapter house and the chamber in which Doomsday Book[4] is deposited. Just within the passage is a small door on the left. To this the verger

---

[1] A Scottish poet (1585–1649).
[2] See Note 1, p. 80.
[3] See Note 1, p. 81.
[4] A book containing the results of a survey of England made by William the Conqueror about 1086. It is now preserved in the Public Record Office in London. It was so called because, upon any difference, the parties received their doom from it.

applied a key; it was double locked, and opened with some difficulty, as if seldom used. We now ascended a dark narrow
staircase, and, passing through a second door, entered the library.

I found myself in a lofty antique hall, the roof supported by
massive joists of old English oak. It was soberly lighted by a
row of Gothic windows at a considerable height from the floor,
and which apparently opened upon the roofs of the cloisters.
An ancient picture of some reverend dignitary of the church in
his robes hung over the fireplace. Around the hall and in a
small gallery were the books, arranged in carved oaken cases.
They consisted principally of old polemical writers, and were
much more worn by time than use. In the center of the library
was a solitary table with two or three books on it, an inkstand
without ink, and a few pens parched by long disuse. The place
seemed fitted for quiet study and profound meditation. It was
buried deep among the massive walls of the abbey, and shut up
from the tumult of the world. I could only hear now and then
the shouts of the schoolboys faintly swelling from the cloisters,
and the sound of a bell tolling for prayers, echoing soberly along
the roofs of the abbey. By degrees the shouts of merriment
grew fainter and fainter, and at length died away; the bell ceased
to toll, and a profound silence reigned through the dusky hall.

I had taken down a little thick quarto, curiously bound in
parchment, with brass clasps, and seated myself at the table in
a venerable elbowchair. Instead of reading, however, I was
beguiled by the solemn monastic air and lifeless quiet of the
place into a train of musing. As I looked around upon the old
volumes in their moldering covers, thus ranged on the shelves,
and apparently never disturbed in their repose, I could not but
consider the library a kind of literary catacomb, where authors,
like mummies, are piously entombed, and left to blacken and
molder in dusty oblivion.

How much, thought I, has each of these volumes, now thrust
aside with such indifference, cost some aching head—how many
weary days! how many sleepless nights! How have their

authors buried themselves in the solitude of cells and cloisters; shut themselves up from the face of man and the still more blessed face of nature; and devoted themselves to painful research and intense reflection! And all for what? To occupy an inch of dusty shelf—to have the title of their works read now and then in a future age by some drowsy churchman or casual straggler like myself; and in another age to be lost, even to remembrance. Such is the amount of this boasted immortality. A mere temporary rumor, a local sound, like the tone of that bell which has just tolled among these towers, filling the ear for a moment—lingering transiently in echo—and then passing away, like a thing that was not!

While I sat half murmuring, half meditating these unprofitable speculations, with my head resting on my hand, I was thrumming with the other hand upon the quarto, until I accidentally loosened the clasps; when, to my utter astonishment, the little book gave two or three yawns, like one awaking from a deep sleep; then a husky hem; and at length began to talk. At first its voice was very hoarse and broken, being much troubled by a cobweb which some studious spider had woven across it; and having probably contracted a cold from long exposure to the chills and damps of the abbey. In a short time, however, it became more distinct, and I soon found it an exceedingly fluent conversable little tome. Its language, to be sure, was rather quaint and obsolete, and its pronunciation, what, in the present day, would be deemed barbarous; but I shall endeavor, as far as I am able, to render it in modern parlance.

It began with railings about the neglect of the world—about merit being suffered to languish in obscurity, and other such commonplace topics of literary repining, and complained bitterly that it had not been opened for more than two centuries; that the Dean only looked now and then into the library, sometimes took down a volume or two, trifled with them for a few moments, and then returned them to their shelves. "What a plague do they mean," said the little quarto, which I began to perceive

was somewhat choleric, " what a plague do they mean by keeping
several thousand volumes of us shut up here, and watched by a
set of old vergers, like so many beauties in a harem, merely to
be looked at now and then by the Dean?   Books were written
to give pleasure and to be enjoyed; and I would have a rule
passed that the Dean should pay each of us a visit at least once
a year; or, if he is not equal to the task, let them once in a while
turn loose the whole School of Westminster among us, that at
any rate we may now and then have an airing."

"Softly, my worthy friend," replied I; "you are not aware
how much better you are off than most books of your generation.
By being stored away in this ancient library, you are like the
treasured remains of those saints and monarchs which lie
enshrined in the adjoining chapels; while the remains of their
contemporary mortals, left to the ordinary course of nature, have
long since returned to dust."

"Sir," said the little tome, ruffling his leaves and looking big,
" I was written for all the world, not for the bookworms of an
abbey.   I was intended to circulate from hand to hand, like
other great contemporary works; but here have I been clasped
up for more than two centuries, and might have silently fallen a
prey to these worms that are playing the very vengeance with
my intestines, if you had not by chance given me an opportunity
of uttering a few last words before I go to pieces."

"My good friend," rejoined I, "had you been left to the
circulation of which you speak, you would long ere this have
been no more.   To judge from your physiognomy, you are now
well stricken in years: very few of your contemporaries can be
at present in existence; and those few owe their longevity to
being immured like yourself in old libraries; which, suffer me to
add, instead of likening to harems, you might more properly
and gratefully have compared to those infirmaries attached to
religious establishments, for the benefit of the old and decrepit,
and where, by quiet fostering and no employment, they often
endure to an amazingly good-for-nothing old age.   You talk of

your contemporaries as if in circulation,—where do we meet
with their works? What do we hear of Robert Groteste of
Lincoln?[1] No one could have toiled harder than he for
immortality. He is said to have written nearly two hundred
volumes. He built, as it were, a pyramid of books to perpetuate
his name; but, alas! the pyramid has long since fallen, and only
a few fragments are scattered in various libraries, where they
are scarcely disturbed even by the antiquarian. What do we
hear of Giraldus Cambrensis,[2] the historian, antiquary, philosopher, theologian, and poet? He declined two bishoprics, that
he might shut himself up and write for posterity: but posterity
never inquires after his labors. What of Henry of Huntingdon,[3]
who, besides a learned history of England, wrote a treatise on
the contempt of the world, which the world has revenged by
forgetting him? What is quoted of Joseph of Exeter,[4] styled
the miracle of his age in classical composition? Of his three
great heroic poems one is lost forever, excepting a mere fragment; the others are known only to a few of the curious in
literature; and as to his love verses and epigrams, they have
entirely disappeared. What is in current use of John Wallis,
the Franciscan, who acquired the name of the tree of life? Of
William of Malmesbury;[5] of Simeon of Durham;[6] of Benedict
of Peterborough;[7] of John Hanvill of St. Albans;[8] of—"

"Prithee, friend," cried the quarto, in a testy tone, "how old

[1] Robert Grosseteste (about 1175–1253), an English ecclesiastic who devoted himself to the suppression of abuses in the church.

[2] Lived about 1146–1220.

[3] Lived about 1084–1155.

[4] Lived about 1200. Considered one of the best mediæval Latin poets in
England.

[5] An English historian and monk, librarian of the monastery at Malmesbury
(about 1095–1142).

[6] An English historian; died about 1130.

[7] Abbot of Peterborough (1177–93), an English historian and ecclesiastic.

[8] A monk of St. Albans about 1190. Author of a Latin poem entitled
Architrenius.

do you think me? You are talking of authors that lived long before my time, and wrote either in Latin or French, so that they in a manner expatriated themselves, and deserved to be forgotten ; [1] but I, sir, was ushered into the world from the press of the renowned Wynkyn de Worde.[2] I was written in my own native tongue, at a time when the language had become fixed ; and, indeed, I was considered a model of pure and elegant English."

(I should observe that these remarks were couched in such intolerably antiquated terms, that I have had infinite difficulty in rendering them into modern phraseology.)

"I cry you mercy," said I, "for mistaking your age ; but it matters little ; almost all the writers of your time have likewise passed into forgetfulness ; and De Worde's publications are mere literary rarities among book collectors. The purity and stability of language, too, on which you found your claims to perpetuity, have been the fallacious dependence of authors of every age, even back to the times of the worthy Robert of Gloucester,[3] who wrote his history in rhymes of Mongrel Saxon.[4] Even now, many talk of Spenser's 'well of pure English undefiled'[5] as if the language ever sprang from a well or fountain head, and was

---

[1] IRVING'S NOTE.—In Latin and French hath many soueraine wittes had great delyte to endyte, and have many noble thinges fulfilde, but certes there ben some that speaken their poisye in French, of which speche the Frenchmen have as good a fantasye as we have in hearying of Frenchmen's Englishe. —*Chaucer's Testament of Love.*

[2] An English printer ; died about 1535. He was an assistant of William Caxton, the first English printer.

[3] An English monk and historian who lived about 1275.

[4] IRVING'S NOTE.—Holinshed, in his Chronicle, observes : "Afterwards, also, by deligent travell of Geffry Chaucer and John Gowre, in the time of Richard the Second, and after them of John Scogan and John Lydgate, monke of Berrie, our said toong was brought to an excellent passe, notwithstanding that it never came unto the type of perfection until the time of Queen Elizabeth, wherein John Jewell, Bishop of Sarum, John Fox, and sundrie learned and excellent writers, have fully accomplished the ornature of the same, to their great praise and immortal commendation."

[5] See Note 1, p. 159.

not rather a mere confluence of various tongues, perpetually subject to changes and intermixtures. It is this which has made English literature so extremely mutable, and the reputation built upon it so fleeting. Unless thought can be committed to something more permanent and unchangeable than such a medium, even thought must share the fate of everything else, and fall into decay. This should serve as a check upon the vanity and exultation of the most popular writer. He finds the language in which he has embarked his fame gradually altering, and subject to the dilapidations of time and the caprice of fashion. He looks back and beholds the early authors of his country, once the favorites of their day, supplanted by modern writers. A few short ages have covered them with obscurity, and their merits can only be relished by the quaint taste of the bookworm. And such, he anticipates, will be the fate of his own work, which, however it may be admired in its day, and held up as a model of purity, will in the course of years grow antiquated and obsolete, until it shall become almost as unintelligible in its native land as an Egyptian obelisk, or one of those Runic inscriptions said to exist in the deserts of Tartary. I declare," added I, with some emotion, "when I contemplate a modern library, filled with new works, in all the bravery of rich gilding and binding, I feel disposed to sit down and weep; like the good Xerxes,[1] when he surveyed his army, pranked out in all the splendor of military array, and reflected that in one hundred years not one of them would be in existence!"

"Ah," said the little quarto, with a heavy sigh, "I see how it is; these modern scribblers have superseded all the good old authors. I suppose nothing is read nowadays but Sir Philip Sydney's 'Arcadia,'[2] Sackville's[3] stately plays, and 'Mirror for

---

[1] King of Persia (519–465 B.C.); attempted the conquest of Greece, but was defeated at Salamis (480 B.C.) and returned to Asia Minor.

[2] See Note 3, p. 162.

[3] Thomas Sackville (1536–1608), an English poet. He became successively Lord Buckhurst and Earl of Dorset.

Magistrates,'[1] or the fine-spun euphuisms of the 'unparalleled John Lyly.'"[2]

"There you are again mistaken," said I; "the writers whom you suppose in vogue, because they happened to be so when you were last in circulation, have long since had their day. Sir Philip Sydney's 'Arcadia,' the immortality of which was so fondly predicted by his admirers,[3] and which, in truth, is full of noble thoughts, delicate images, and graceful turns of language, is now scarcely ever mentioned. Sackville has strutted into obscurity; and even Lyly, though his writings were once the delight of a court, and apparently perpetuated by a proverb, is now scarcely known even by name. A whole crowd of authors who wrote and wrangled at the time have likewise gone down, with all their writings and their controversies. Wave after wave of succeeding literature has rolled over them, until they are buried so deep that it is only now and then that some industrious diver after fragments of antiquity brings up a specimen for the gratification of the curious.

"For my part," I continued, "I consider this mutability of language a wise precaution of Providence for the benefit of the world at large, and of authors in particular. To reason from analogy: we daily behold the varied and beautiful tribes of vegetables springing up, flourishing, adorning the fields for a short time, and then fading into dust, to make way for their successors. Were not this the case, the fecundity of nature would be a griev-

---

[1] A compilation of poems begun in 1555. It consisted of biographies of men in high places who had come to violent ends. The stanzas which Sackville contributed to this collection far exceed the rest in value.

[2] See Note 2, p. 13.

[3] IRVING'S NOTE.—"Live ever sweete booke; the simple image of his gentle witt, and the golden pillar of his noble courage; and ever notify unto the world that thy writer was the secretary of eloquence, the breath of the muses, the honey bee of the daintyest flowers of witt and arte, the pith or morale and the intellectual virtues, the arme of Bellona in the field, the tongue of Suada in the chamber, the spirite of Practise in esse, and the paragon of excellency in print."—*Harvey's Pierce's Supererogation.*

ance instead of a blessing. The earth would groan with rank and excessive vegetation, and its surface become a tangled wilderness. In like manner, the works of genius and learning decline and make way for subsequent productions. Language gradually varies, and with it fade away the writings of authors who have flourished their allotted time; otherwise, the creative powers of genius would overstock the world, and the mind would be completely bewildered in the endless mazes of literature. Formerly there were some restraints on this excessive multiplication. Works had to be transcribed by hand, which was a slow and laborious operation; they were written either on parchment, which was expensive, so that one work was often erased to make way for another; or on papyrus, which was fragile and extremely perishable. Authorship was a limited and unprofitable craft, pursued chiefly by monks in the leisure and solitude of their cloisters. The accumulation of manuscripts was slow and costly, and confined almost entirely to monasteries. To these circumstances it may, in some measure, be owing that we have not been inundated by the Intellect of antiquity; that the fountains of thought have not been broken up, and modern genius drowned in the deluge. But the inventions of paper and the press have put an end to all these restraints. They have made every one a writer, and enabled every mind to pour itself into print, and diffuse itself over the whole intellectual world. The consequences are alarming. The stream of literature has swollen into a torrent —augmented into a river—expanded into a sea. A few centuries since, five or six hundred manuscripts constituted a great library; but what would you say to libraries, such as actually exist, containing three or four hundred thousand volumes; legions of authors at the same time busy; and the press going on with fearfully increasing activity, to double and quadruple the number? Unless some unforeseen mortality should break out among the progeny of the muse, now that she has become so prolific, I tremble for posterity. I fear the mere fluctuation of language will not be sufficient. Criticism may do much; it increases

with the increase of literature, and resembles one of those salu-
tary checks on population spoken of by economists. All possible
encouragement, therefore, should be given to the growth of
critics, good or bad. But I fear all will be in vain; let criticism
do what it may, writers will write, printers will print, and the
world will inevitably be overstocked with good books. It will
soon be the employment of a lifetime merely to learn their
names. Many a man of passable information at the present day
reads scarcely anything but reviews, and before long a man of
erudition will be little better than a mere walking catalogue."

"My very good sir," said the little quarto, yawning most
drearily in my face, "excuse my interrupting you, but I perceive
you are rather given to prose. I would ask the fate of an author
who was making some noise just as I left the world. His reputation, however, was considered quite temporary. The learned
shook their heads at him, for he was a poor half-educated varlet,
that knew little of Latin, and nothing of Greek, and had been
obliged to run the country for deer-stealing.[1] I think his name
was Shakespeare. I presume he soon sunk into oblivion."

"On the contrary," said I, "it is owing to that very man that
the literature of his period has experienced a duration beyond the
ordinary term of English literature. There rise authors now and
then, who seem proof against the mutability of language, because
they have rooted themselves in the unchanging principles of
human nature. They are like gigantic trees that we sometimes
see on the banks of a stream, which, by their vast and deep
roots, penetrating through the mere surface, and laying hold on
the very foundations of the earth, preserve the soil around them
from being swept away by the overflowing current, and hold up
many a neighboring plant, and, perhaps, worthless weed, to perpetuity. Such is the case with Shakespeare, whom we behold,
defying the encroachments of time, retaining in modern use the
language and literature of his day, and giving duration to many
an indifferent author merely from having flourished in his vicinity.

[1] See p. 172.

But even he, I grieve to say, is gradually assuming the tint of age, and his whole form is overrun by a profusion of commentators, who, like clambering vines and creepers, almost bury the noble plant that upholds them."

Here the little quarto began to heave his sides and chuckle, until at length he broke out into a plethoric fit of laughter that had wellnigh choked him, by reason of his excessive corpulency. "Mighty well!" cried he, as soon as he could recover breath, "mighty well! and so you would persuade me that the literature of an age is to be perpetuated by a vagabond deer-stealer! by a man without learning! by a poet, forsooth—a poet!" And here he wheezed forth another fit of laughter.

I confess that I felt somewhat nettled at this rudeness, which, however, I pardoned on account of his having flourished in a less polished age. I determined, nevertheless, not to give up my point.

"Yes," resumed I positively, "a poet; for of all writers he has the best chance for immortality. Others may write from the head, but he writes from the heart, and the heart will always understand him. He is the faithful portrayer of nature, whose features are always the same, and always interesting. Prose writers are voluminous and unwieldy; their pages are crowded with commonplaces, and their thoughts expanded into tediousness. But with the true poet everything is terse, touching, or brilliant. He gives the choicest thoughts in the choicest language. He illustrates them by everything that he sees most striking in nature and art. He enriches them by pictures of human life, such as it is passing before him. His writings, therefore, contain the spirit, the aroma, if I may use the phrase, of the age in which he lives. They are caskets which inclose within a small compass the wealth of the language—its family jewels, which are thus transmitted in a portable form to posterity. The setting may occasionally be antiquated, and require now and then to be renewed, as in the case of Chaucer; [1] but the brilliancy

1 Geoffrey Chaucer (1340–1400), the first great English poet, author of the Canterbury Tales.

and intrinsic value of the gems continue unaltered. Cast a look back over the long reach of literary history. What vast valleys of dullness, filled with monkish legends and academical controversies! What bogs of theological speculations; what dreary wastes of metaphysics! Here and there only do we behold the heaven-illuminated bards, elevated like beacons on their widely-separated heights, to transmit the pure light of poetical intelligence from age to age." [1]

I was just about to launch forth into eulogiums upon the poets of the day, when the sudden opening of the door caused me to turn my head. It was the verger, who came to inform me that it was time to close the library. I sought to have a parting word with the quarto, but the worthy little tome was silent; the clasps were closed; and it looked perfectly unconscious of all that had passed. I have been to the library two or three times since, and have endeavored to draw it into further conversation, but in vain: and whether all this rambling colloquy actually took place, or whether it was another of those odd daydreams to which I am subject, I have never to this moment been able to discover.

[1] IRVING'S NOTE. —

> " Thorow [2] earth and waters deepe,
>   The pen by skill doth passe:
> And featly [3] nyps the worldes abuse,
>   And shoes us in a glasse,
> The vertu and the vice
>   Of every wight alyve;
> The honey comb that bee doth make,
>   Is not so sweet in hyve,
> As are the golden leves
>   That drops from poet's head;
> Which doth surmount our common talke,
>   As farre as dross doth lead."

Churchyard. [4]

[2] **Through.**   [3] Deftly.

[4] Thomas Churchyard (1520–1604), an English poet, author of many miscellaneous works.

SUGGESTIONS FOR THE STUDY OF THE SKETCH-BOOK

Among possible methods of approach in the study of *The Sketch-Book* those of most value seem to be: first, that of literary appreciation; second, that of literary art or practice; and third, that of rhetoric. Each of these three should begin with impression, and end, as far as the formal study is concerned, with expression in the form of oral and written composition. The aim of the first is to help the student to enjoy *The Sketch-Book* in particular and to make him in general more susceptible to literary suggestion. The aim of the second is the same as the aim of the first, and in addition it endeavors to give the pupil some knowledge of literary art and some skill in its practice. The aim of the third is to provide the student with rhetorical drill. From each of these points of view each paper in *The Sketch-Book* could be studied with profit. As regards the first method of approach it is certainly advisable that the teacher take whatever means he can to make his pupils as sensitive as possible to the peculiar literary values of each individual paper, for adequate literary appreciation, considered for its own sake and for the sake of what comes of it, is the chief end of the study of literature. The words of a great author are mere notation, like notes in music, until they find a response in men's memories and feelings. With different pupils the response varies as much as does music produced by different types of instruments. Only a teacher of literature knows how little some pupils obtain from a classic and how varied is the response of even those who are most sensitive to literary suggestion.

It is advisable, therefore, that various possible interpretations of the paper as a whole and of separate passages should be discussed and appraised. Humor and pathos should not be passed by as self-evident but should be noted. Onomatopœia and beauty of rhythm should oftentimes be pointed out, for those who read ephemeral writers are frequently unaware of the compressed riches of classic literature. Finally, and most important, the teacher should secure from the members of the class personal comment and oral and written composition; he should endeavor to relate the student's experience to the thoughts of the author; he should try so to associate, intermingle, and weave, the moods and memories of the pupil with the images and ideas of Irving that there will be no line of demarcation between what is contributed by the author and what is contributed by the student. If the teacher can do this he will have taught the pupil to do creative reading, which is literary appreciation.

In like manner each selection from *The Sketch-Book* should be studied from the point of view of literary art. Pupils should learn from their study of this work that the effects produced by the words of Irving are not due to luck or chance but to art. They should discover that art consists in using means to an end; they should determine the means that Irving has used to produce the results he has obtained; and they should endeavor by use of similar means to secure similar results.

Not every paper, however, should be studied from the point of view of rhetoric. To make each paper the basis of extended rhetorical drill would be tiresome and unprofitable. It is equally bad to maintain that because *The Sketch-Book* is classic literature it is sacrilege to use any portion of it for rhetorical analysis. Students sufficiently advanced to appreciate Irving are not so lacking in discrimination as to dislike all the essays in *The Sketch-Book* because unpleasant tasks are associated with some of them or to condemn the entire study of literature because certain parts of that study are disagreeable. Drill used to form a habit always lacks variety and apart from its end is disagreeable. Drill, nevertheless, is indispensable because of the economics it affords the student in time and effort. With most classes, furthermore, the final result of rhetorical analysis and drill is a higher appreciation of literature. For these reasons some but not all the papers should be studied from the point of view of rhetoric.

Irving's paragraphs are usually formed so carefully that it is worth while for the student to point out topic-sentences, if any; to indicate by what means the paragraphs are developed from the topic-sentences; to suggest other ways in which the topic-sentences might have been developed; to criticize the unity of the paragraphs; to determine whether Irving in addition to topic paragraphs makes use of summarizing or transitional paragraphs. He should ascertain whether any such paragraphs could with profit be joined either to the paragraph that precedes or the paragraph that follows and whether Irving either consciously or unconsciously has adopted a standard length for his ordinary paragraphs. Is the length influenced by content?

He should inquire whether Irving uses paragraphs, sentences, clauses, phrases, words, or mere continuity or logic, most commonly in making transitions from paragraph to paragraph. Is coherence between sentences assisted by the use of pronouns, adverbs, conjunctions, echo, and synonyms? For pronouns the student may substitute antecedents and ascertain the degree of clearness with which the former refer to the latter. He should notice how skillfully Irving avoids disagreeable repetitions through the use of synonyms and synonymous expressions. Do not the beginnings and endings of Irving's sentences, the attractive cadences, often cover defects in emphasis and transition? Would not his style furnish a better model if some of the loose sentences were given a periodic form? Such inquiry, directed first to the work of Irving and then to the pupil's own composition, is a valuable means of acquiring facility in the management of the elements of style.

SUGGESTIVE EXERCISES

The following questions are intended to assist in the development of literary appreciation and literary practice.

The Author's Account of Himself

1. Why did Irving follow the example of Addison in *The Spectator* and give an account of the author in the first essay of the series?

2. What according to the author were the chief incentives that made him wish to travel?

3. Select from this essay four of the best examples of Irving's humor.

4. Name as exactly as possible the prevailing mood in which this essay is written.

5. Select from the essay the expressions which you think are most effective in indicating or creating this mood.

6. Why do so few modern tourists carry a sketch-book?

7. What does Irving say in this paper that makes one wish to read the sketches that follow?

THE VOYAGE

1. Could Irving's expression, "the reveries of a sea voyage," be used to indicate accurately the character of this sketch?

2. Do the author's meditations during the voyage prepare him in any way to visit Europe?

3. Enumerate the various states of feeling through which the author passes during the voyage.

4. What attitude toward the reader does the author assume in this paper?

5. Discover if you can why the not improbable incident of the sick sailor seems inartistic and out of place.

6. Does this paper help to increase our interest in the sketches that follow, or in Geoffrey Crayon?

7. What in the sketch is as characteristic to-day of an ocean voyage as it was when Irving wrote?

8. In Irving's style supplement this sketch with paragraphs giving a traveler's feelings during an ocean voyage of to-day.

CHRISTMAS

1. What change from *The Voyage* has occurred in *Christmas* as regards the attitude of the author toward the reader.

2. What in this essay is introductory to the Christmas papers that follow?

3. What has the style of this essay gained from the use of periodic sentences, numerous allusions, elaborate figures of speech, and studied diction? What has it lost?

THE STAGECOACH

1. Is this paper written merely as an introduction to the Bracebridge papers that follow?

2. Was Irving successful in putting on "the genuine holiday spirit"?

3. Is it diction or the selection of details that makes the paragraph on page 33 so vivid and picturesque?

4. Do you approve of Irving's use of the grove of trees on page 35?

5. Analyze the description of the inn for point of view, fundamental image, and arrangement of details.

CHRISTMAS EVE

1. Is the chief object of this paper to tell a story, or to present the Squire's character, or to portray old English customs?

2. Describe the hall and explain its use.

3. What are the characteristic traits of Squire Bracebridge?

4. What are the characteristic traits of Simon?

5. What makes Irving's humor at the top of page 49 less successful than that on pages 13–15?

6. In what respect is the conclusion of the paper artistic?

7. Why did Irving lay the scene of his *Christmas Eve* in moonlight, in an antiquated dwelling, far from the highway?

CHRISTMAS DAY

1. To what extent do description, humor, story, characters, and touches of human nature, each contribute to the interest of this paper?

2. Study the descriptive paragraph on page 51 for fundamental image and for the selection and arrangement of details.

3. Elaborate the description of the choir

THE CHRISTMAS DINNER

1. Does Irving seem equally interested in characters of various ages? Compare him in this respect with other authors.

2. Was Irving following the rules of legitimate art if he created the character of the Squire and then slyly laughed at him, hoping that he himself might thereby escape adverse criticism for presenting to his readers so many details derived from antiquarian research?

3. What was Irving's purpose in writing a group of papers on subjects connected with Christmas in England?

WESTMINSTER ABBEY

1. How does this account and that given in *Stratford-on-Avon* differ essentially from the account given in the ordinary guidebook?

2. If this sketch is intended to be more than a mere description of Westminster Abbey, express in a sentence what it signifies.

3. What did the author take with him when he left Westminster Abbey?

4. The Spectator visited the Abbey with Sir Roger de Coverley. Why did Geoffrey Crayon go alone?

5. Did Irving choose, since he was familiar with Westminster Abbey, the best season, hour, and point of approach, to make his visit effective with the reader? Would it not have been as well to have passed in at the main entrance and have heard the organ music in mid-afternoon and have passed out through the cloisters at twilight?

6. Select the best three paragraphs and attempt to determine to what extent their excellence is due to precision of diction, onomatopœia, melody, figures of speech, connotation of words or phrases, and selection of details.

7. Collect from the essay all the synonyms for Westminster Abbey and add more of your own coining.

THE LEGEND OF SLEEPY HOLLOW

1. Consider the quotations that Irving affixed to the various sketches. Would it be well to have the custom come again into style?

2. Explain exactly how the mood or atmosphere that pervades this story is different from that found in *Westminster Abbey*.

3. Why would you find it more difficult to imitate successfully the style of this story than the style of *Westminster Abbey?*

4. Is the great charm of this story due chiefly to plot, character, description, or to general humor?

5. Determine to what extent the humor of this sketch depends upon incongruous associations occurring in comparisons, similes, and metaphors.

6. What devices does Irving use near the beginning of the story to arouse the interest, curiosity, or expectation of the reader?

7. As a literary device is Mr. Knickerbocker in *The Legend of Sleepy Hollow* as useful as Squire Bracebridge in the Christmas papers?

8. Why was Irving unwilling to have the reader believe that Crane was a cruel potentate?

9. Compare the connotation of the figures of speech used in describing the physical appearance of Ichabod with the connotation of the figures used in describing Katrina.

10. Was Ichabod's uncontrollable terror at the appearance of the goblin properly prepared for by Irving?

11. Would this story have been better had Crane's character been depicted more largely through his deeds and less by means of the author's comments?

12. Why did Ichabod leave Sleepy Hollow?

13. Irving seems to excel in soliloquy or meditation rather than in dialogue. Would this story have been better had it contained more conversation?

14. Would the story be better if any part of it were omitted?

15. Are the rhetorical rules for description exemplified in the account of Van Tassel's farm?

Rip Van Winkle

1. What purpose is served by the description of the fairy mountains?

2. Why did the women of the village take Rip's part?

3. What means does Irving take in spite of Rip's faults to secure for him the reader's sympathy?

4. Write a list of adjectives that will serve to indicate the character of Rip.

5. Indicate the extent to which Rip's character determines the course of the story.

6. Does Irving represent the appearance of Henry Hudson and his crew as Rip's dream? Is the incident joined too vaguely with the rest of the story?

7. Did Irving select wisely the date when Rip was supposed to fall asleep?

8. Why at the close of the story did Rip prefer the company of the rising generation to that of his old cronies?

9. Have the sound of Irving's words anything to do with the pathos when Rip in his ruined home called loudly for his wife and children?

10. To secure a humorous effect in the drama called *Rip Van Winkle* Rip speaks in Dutch dialect and even his dog has been renamed Schneider. Would such changes improve Irving's story?

11. Is Irving a realist who truthfully presents all he sees whether lovely or unlovely?

12. Compare Irving's characters with those of other authors with which you are familiar and attempt to determine whether the creatures of Irving's fancy are mere types or are real individuals.

The Wife

1. Is it fair to say that Irving, or Geoffrey Crayon, in this essay has assumed toward the reader and toward Leslie a disagreeable air of superior knowledge?

2. Would not the story have been more effective had it been told by Leslie?

3. Is not the conclusion arranged so tritely as to be almost theatrical?

4. Is the moral sufficiently well pointed to redeem the sketch?

5. Is it possible that the theme of this sketch has with the lapse of years become so hackneyed that it cannot now affect readers as it once did?

The Art of Book-Making

1. Point out means by which Irving arouses the curiosity or expectation of the reader?

2. Has Irving in this paper made use of literary devices especially suited to readers who are interested in literary subjects?

3. Is Irving seeking in this paper to promote a reform?

4. If Irving practices the art of book-making ought he to be censured?

5. Contrast the style of this essay with that of *Westminster Abbey*.

6. Is the dream device in literature worn out?

Stratford-On-Avon

1. Write a sub-title that will indicate the character of this essay.

2. Is the mood or atmosphere adapted to the season and hour as well in this sketch as in *Westminster Abbey?*

3. What is Irving's attitude toward Shakespeare and his works?

4. Is Irving usually in sympathy with his surroundings?

5. What is Irving's attitude toward the reader? His personality is charming. Is it here less obtrusive than in *The Wife?* Is this a matter that can be controlled by literary art?

6. Can you determine now the chief sources of the charm of Irving's style?

7. In which is Irving's imagination more apparent, in *Stratford on Avon* or in *The Legend of Sleepy Hollow?*

The Mutability of Literature

1. What is the fundamental idea on which this paper is based?

2. Make a summary of this sketch and of *The Art of Book-Making* to determine whether summaries can contain what is valuable in these papers.

3. What means does Irving take to give a natural introduction to his train of musing?

4. Taking into consideration Irving's skill in the management of literary meditation do you think he would have done better to have rejected the device of the dream and have presented his ideas in the form of a reverie in a library?

5. Write the future history of a school publication which has been deposited in a great library.

6. Did Irving prepare properly for the quarto's question concerning Shakespeare?

7. Is any work of man more durable than literature?

ADDITIONAL TOPICS FOR ORAL AND WRITTEN COMPOSITION

1. Geoffrey Crayon's First Visit to Harlem.
2. Shall we Travel in Europe or in America?
3. The Captain's Account of Irving.
4. Tourists' Fashions in the Time of Irving.
5. Modern Fashions in Traveling.
6. An Ocean Voyage.
7. Can Science Impair the Poetry of the Sea?
8. Our Old Home.
9. An Emigrant's Feelings on Coming to America.
10. A History of the Celebration of Thanksgiving Day.
11. A History of the Celebration of the Fourth of July.
12. Christmas, Old and New.
13. Christmas in the City.
14. Christmas on the Farm.
15. The Stagecoach, as Told by One of the Schoolboys.
16. The Waits and Other Christmas Singers.
17. A Ride in the Street Car on the Day before Christmas.
18. The Modern Coachman.

19. The Old English Hall.
20. Old Christmas Games.
21. A Prank of the Blue-eyed Romp.
22. Simon's Visit to the Widow.
23. Winter in England.
24. An Ideal Celebration of Christmas.
25. A Visit to a Famous Building.
26. The History of Westminster Abbey.
27. The Hall of Fame.
28. A Visit to Sleepy Hollow.
29. A Tale of the Highlands of the Hudson.
30. Ichabod's Last Talk with Katrina.
31. Brom Bones's Confession.
32. In the Haunts of Rip Van Winkle.
33. An Adventure of Rip, the Younger.
34. A Modern Pilgrimage with Ben Franklin.
35. A Spring Morning with Irving.
36. A Letter from Stratford.
37. A Pilgrimage to Sunnyside.